DAWN OF
A NEW ERA

DIVALDO FRANCO

DAWN OF A NEW ERA

By the Spirit
Manoel Philomeno de Miranda

ISBN: 978-1-942408-97-0

Original title in Portuguese:
Amanhecer de uma Nova Era
(Brazil, 2012)

Translated by: Darrell W. Kimble and Ily Reis
Cover design by: Cláudio Urpia
Layout: Rones José Silvano de Lima – www.bookebooks.com.br
Edited by: Rones José Silvano de Lima – www.bookebooks.com.br

Edition of
LEAL PUBLISHER
8425 Biscayne Blvd. Ste. 104
Miami, FL 33138, USA
www.lealpublisher.com
(305) 306-6447

Authorized edition by Centro Espírita Caminho da Redenção – Salvador (BA) – Brazil

INTERNATIONAL DATA FOR CATALOGING IN PUBLICATION (ICP)

F895d   Franco, Divaldo (1927)

      Dawn of a new era / By Spirit Author Manoel Philomeno de Miranda [psychographed by] Divaldo Pereira Franco ; translated by Darrel W. Kimble and Ily Reis – Miami (FL), USA : Leal Publisher, 2018.

      202 p.; 21cm

      Original title: *Amanhecer de uma Nova Era*

      ISBN: 978-1-942408-97-0

      1. Spiritism 2. Mediumship. I Franco, Divaldo Pereira, 1927 – II. Title.

CDD 133.9

CONTENTS

INTRODUCTION

Since remotest times, the high-order Guides of humanity have stated that the earth is a planet of blessed trials and expiations for its inhabitants. It is a planet composed not only of spirits undergoing intellectual and moral growth, but also of those who have committed wrongs against the Divine Laws that govern the universe.

From one aspect, the earth is a school that fosters the development of incomparable treasures that lie dormant in the innermost folds of individuals, helping them break free from primitivism and the coarser sensations in order to acquire the sanctifying and liberating emotions for which they are destined, providing them the opportunity of union with the Divine Thought.

This phase of afflictions, however, would be limited in time and space, for it must give way to a period of renewal, hope, lasting peace and well-being, foretelling an era of plenitude and harmony.

Depending on the behavior of the individuals that inhabit the planetary school, the time would come when suffering and despair would give way to different resources, those that promote evolution without the tears or misfortunes that lacerate the sentiments and sometimes pervert those who are unprepared for the school's invaluable lessons.

Throughout the millions of years of anthropological, sociological and psychological evolution that has enabled human beings to understand countless cosmic laws that govern life and foster intellectual-moral achievement, it has become easier to acquire the balance that promotes the awakening to their spiritual reality so that they may pursue broader and lovelier horizons on the unending journey toward love.

Plagued by constant suffering over the millennia, they have found no other alternative, except self-enlightenment as the sure way for moving beyond their current evolutionary level.

Revelations from the spirit world have been incessant; they have never failed to enlighten human consciousness regarding its eternality, an endeavor which began in the distant past and remained shrouded in mystery because of consciousness's level of evolution. But now, in these glorious days of lucid and easy communication with high-order spirits, human consciousness is discovering invaluable behaviors that lead to the inner access of the kingdom of heaven.

There has never been an absence of harmonizing guidelines for human beings — who, immersed in the physical body, easily fall prey to error or fear, lose heart, or run from responsibility — to provide them with the conditions required for promoting real freedom, stimulating them to soar in the direction of triumphant immortality.

At the present stage of the psychological process, human beings have, as a result of the incomparable contribution of Spiritism,[1] which has demystified death and unveiled the realities beyond the material cloud, a better understanding of what their

---

[1]   Spiritism is a science that deals with the nature, origin and destiny of spirits, and their relationship with the corporeal world. *What is Spiritism*, Allan Kardec (International Spiritist Council, 2010)

existential purpose is, its conditionings and events, its impositions and necessities, expanding their potential for self-encounter, self-awareness and existential logic...

Disciplined mediumship that is oriented to the good has caused so-called mysteries[2] to shed their intricate garments and be divested of magic and the supernatural, thus becoming character-shaping disciplines capable of promoting the exchange between the two vibratory planes – the material and the spiritual – naturally and sublimely.

At the same time, this enables human beings, always in need of help, to rise to the level of coworker, aiding and assisting spirits ignorant of their reality, thus decreasing the swarm of miserable discarnate spirits who are in sickly partnership with incarnate wanderers...

This knowledge has done away with many of the enigmas and encumbrances that have always hindered individual and collective progress due to the torments of afflicting obsessions[3] that continue to comprise a dreadful pandemic.

Once the immortality that awaits everyone is unveiled, human beings' existential psychological goal changes from having to being, from temporary to permanent, from apparent to real.

Anesthetizing illusions, exhaustive pleasures, deceitful honors, and community recognition, devoid of fulfilling meaning, are no longer satisfying.

Their aspirations automatically shift from today to eternity, from the tormenting moment of desire to the quiet enjoyment of peace, from the deception that offers things but becomes merciless guilt that drives its victims to various disorders...

---

[2]   Communications with the spirit world. – I.R.

[3]   "Obsession ... the domination that certain spirits acquire over certain individuals." Allan Kardec, *The Mediums' Book*, Ch. XXIII, #237 (International Spiritist Council). – I.R.

Physical existence, under whatever conditions, offers direction, a profound reason to be experienced with joy and emotional definition.

The earth is going through a great transition in every aspect.

Exhausted humans knock on heaven's door, pleading for support. In response, the Divinity grants them the blessings of work and enlightenment in order that they may free themselves from their oppression.

Threats of the extinction of life are vanishing such that evil and instruments of harm and destruction may also vanish, making way for new attitudes and different resources for sublimation.

High-order spirits from another dimension are descending into the earthly darkness in answer to Jesus' summons in order to contribute on behalf of their brothers and sisters that are still lagging behind during this great and decisive moment in which they have the chance to ascend with their beloved Mother Earth to enjoy the blessings of cosmic harmony for all Her inhabitants.

Challenges, sudden changes in behavior, and a number of bitter struggles involving the domineering past against the promising future mark this period.

Nonetheless, the presence of the Sublime Galilean consoles all who may seek Him and try to connect with His ineffable love, occasioning the joy of living and well-being in any situation.

The darkness of ignorance is vanishing, although some short-lived abuses still remain.

The victory of love and the good has become incontestable, and the dawn of a new era is triumphantly taking shape.

This book was written from the heart. It depicts a number of spirits engaged in activities that assist workers of the good — momentarily attacked by the forces of spiritual wickedness — under the sweet and gentle command of Saint Francis of Assisi, the emulator of Jesus who, in dark times, implemented on earth a period of tenderness and fraternity, although everything conspired against it.

We hope that these pages may encourage those who are struggling, help the indifferent arrive at a decision, aid in the preparation for forthcoming days, and act as a kindly invitation to joy and peace.

MANOEL PHILOMENO DE MIRANDA
Dubai, UAE, February 14, 2012.

NEW RESPONSIBILITIES

In our spirit community, as indeed in all others, work is an ongoing blessing that motivates us to develop dormant moral qualities, inviting us to inner growth for achieving plenitude.

Along with our daily tasks, we take part in endeavors of support and encouragement for the progress of our beloved earth and its inhabitants, especially during this time of great revolutions announcing its moral transition.

Invariably, at night, after we have completed our tasks, we attend study sessions, conferences and discussions on intellectual and moral development in order to acquire knowledge to be used during our own evolutionary experiences, or we meditate on life and all of God's wonderful gifts.

Thus, from time to time we are invited to participate in specific labors, particularly those that involve our incarnate brothers and sisters. This is a great honor and it encourages us to continue such renewing activities.

On one such occasion, when the heavens were embroidered with stellar archipelagos, displaying a small portion of cosmic glory, I was in the garden of our colony's central amphitheater, pondering the mercy of the Father

Creator and observing passersby also fascinated by the wonder of nature, when a devoted worker from the Department of Communications approached.

He seemed absolutely jubilant. Always kindly, he had become an excellent worker who excelled in his faithfulness to duty. He was also a dear friend. While he was in the physical body he had experienced the greatness of the Spiritist revelation, and over the course of his life he had left luminous footprints of love and charity as an effective medium and wise instructor.

Alongside other sowers of the Spiritist Doctrine in the first half of the 20th century, he had carried out a worthy ministry involving his loving spiritual assistance, and which continues to this very day.

He possessed inestimable credits, and I was always enriched by the conversations we had whenever possible, when he would shed light on some of my questions.

On this particular occasion, he brought me an invitation from a benevolent mentor in the area of communications to join a team that would remain in the physical world for a significant period of time, working alongside spirit-guides on behalf of those who are devoted to the good and who work for the progress of humankind.

Dear Hildebrando informed me that the fierce enemy of Christianity, who inhabited a dismal area of the spirit world, forming teams to persecute Spiritist Christians, was preparing for a wicked assault against a venerable Spiritist institution as an act of revenge for having been unmasked in a farce he had devised.[4]

---

[4] See chapter 20 (Confrontation with the Darkness) in our book *Planetary Transition* (LEAL Publisher, 2016). – Spirit Author.

I immediately recalled the incident because I had participated in it with a number of good friends involved in the mediumistic endeavor. My curiosity was aroused, so I asked:

"Will the attack have dreadful consequences for the workers of Jesus?"

"No doubt," he answered gravely. "As you know, evil is enrooted in the heart of those who adopt it, the natural consequence of having embraced arrogance and pride for a long time. Because the former rabbi has been unable to unleash morbid energies on those he believes to be his enemies, he is holding on to the idea of revenge until an opportunity presents itself. Moreover, other endeavors have been scheduled in addition to assisting him and his minions."

And to add some more information, he continued:

"Our incarnate coworkers often forget that the physical and spirit worlds interpenetrate each other. The two do not have definite boundaries, and this allows for constant exchange between their inhabitants. Although they were forewarned about the need for vigilance, once they become immersed in the physical body they quickly begin to indulge in aggressive attitudes and behaviors that are completely different from the way they ought to live, thus attuning to wicked spirits and opening the way for their interference through obsession[5]...

"They may be excellent theorists about what is going on around them, but when it comes to issues that directly harm their interests, they give in to resentment, to anger that turns into rage and poisons them, which makes them easy to control by spirits whom they should resist with dignifying deeds.

"Pride – that spurious child of selfishness – is the great adversary of human beings, who think themselves special,

---

[5] See footnote 2 above. – I.R.

and always deserving of respect and consideration, even though they do not offer the same to those whom they see as enemies. Foolish and immature, they create situations that are difficult to resolve because of the way they handle issues that should be addressed with fraternal understanding and real friendship.

"And since they possess a sickly sensibility, they harbor resentments and shout insanely whenever they are contradicted, opening their vibratory fields to the influence of vile, perturbing and mocking spirits who connect with them and lead them to act wrongly toward their neighbor, whom they should love and understand, thus compromising the work of the group they belong to. Not a few upstanding institutions with lofty goals for building a better world fail due to this interference by idle and vengeful spirits, and they end up wasting the entire effort of the selfless spirit-mentors and dedicated missionaries who collaborate with them... As long as Gospel workers do not have a responsible awareness – one that can overcome selfishness and the need to project their own image – the gigantic battle will continue."

After a short pause, he added:

"Tomorrow at 8:00 p.m. we will have a meeting at the Department of Communications to study and get details concerning an endeavor that will be under the blessings of the apostle Saint Francis of Assisi, whom a venerable spirit, dedicated to serving Jesus on the physical plane, has called on to assist us."

He said goodbye, leaving me with the fragrance of his goodness and the magnetism of his spiritual superiority.

His words had resonated immediately within my being, as I had often witnessed their effectiveness in dealing with obsessions and persecutions by spirits.

Despite their knowledge about the Spiritist Doctrine and the wiles and skills of obviously wretched spirits of low morality, but who, nonetheless, have a high capacity for discernment and persecutory action, some of Spiritism's weaker adherents do not apply the Doctrine to their own behavior. Thus they become easy prey for their discarnate foes and others who consider themselves to be opponents of Jesus, taking pleasure in creating obstacles and complications in the harvest field where they are working.

These adherents begin their work with great enthusiasm, planning the transformation of the terrestrial planet and its psychosphere, but as time passes and as they settle into their routine, their excitement wanes and they become aware of the difficulties, especially in relationships with others. Consequently they fail at their own requisite spiritual renewal.

Were they to spend more time pondering Master Jesus' invaluable lessons, which urge us to be continuously watchful and prayerful, and study the sure guidelines of Allan Kardec[6] contained in the Codification,[7] as well as the contents of mediumistic communications – considering them not only beautiful, but above all, carriers of serious teachings worthy of the highest consideration – they would certainly be more successful at resisting troublesome situations.

Of course the evolutionary process occurs through challenges and difficulties that result from past behaviors.

Assuming foolish attitudes of revenge and mistrust toward their brothers and sisters in the faith and toward their friends in doctrinal activities, the afore-mentioned individuals

---

[6] Allan Kardec (1804-1869) - Codifier of Spiritism. – I.R.

[7] Kardec's Codification comprises five books: *The Spirits' Book, The Mediums' Book, The Gospel according to Spiritism, Heaven and Hell,* and *Genesis* (International Spiritist Council editions) – I.R.

become stumbling blocks for everyone after poisoning themselves with unhealthy thoughts and mental fixations whenever they are disappointed or dissatisfied.

It is always well-advised – as the high-order spirits recommend – to personally heed the counsels that flow down from the higher spheres, instead of applying them to one's neighbor. However that is not what usually happens, and major setbacks threaten the flowering of the great harvest of the Master, as happened long ago when the governance of the Roman Empire passed on to His servants. Due to the immediate favors one could enjoy, Caesar became more attractive than God, and self-sacrifice through love was relegated to the background, allowing the adulteration of the beautiful and austere teachings Christians had received from those who preceded them in martyrdom.

Thus nascent Christianity experienced the decadence of its purposes and the adulteration of its teachings, and it let itself be overcome by idolatry and the pagan rituals of the past, although by different names.

Spiritism, in turn, has been shaken by internal turmoil, creating dissensions – those endearing children of pride – and has reached the point of challenging the foundations of the Codification, or presenting false techniques disguised as scientific but coming from personal experience and mediumistic information unconfirmed by the universality of the teaching.

New "missionaries" are constantly showing up, touting their lofty achievements; however, they are immersed in tormenting obsessions deriving from fascination.[8] Moreover,

---

[8]   "… a delusion created directly by a spirit in the thoughts of a medium, which in a certain manner paralyzes his or her capacity to judge the quality of the communications. Fascinated mediums do not believe themselves to be deceived." Allan Kardec, *The Mediums' Book*, Ch. XXIII, #239. (ISC, 2007). – I.R.

preposterous novelties are presented that cause ridicule to the good name of the Doctrine because of the way such unfortunate theses are expounded, born, as they are, in the vanity of those who are mediums or not.

In fact, these are very delicate times because all spheres of terrestrial activity face the same confusion caused by those interested in preserving instability, which has reached high levels of crime and violence, horror and senselessness...

It is imperative to return to the evangelical sources and origins of the doctrinal movement free of the grip of authorities, specialists, holders of university degrees and intellectual arrogance, and to return to simplicity and to eminently Christian service.

As I pondered the matter, I was thrilled at the sight of the glittering constellations at immeasurable distances, extolling the greatness of Love.

I listened to the pulsation of nature in majestic display, inviting an analysis of its causality and purpose, demanding, of course, respect and veneration to the All-Merciful and Loving Father.

As I contemplated the earth immersed in the darkness of the night, I could also see lights, like votive candles of gratitude to the Creator, indicating centers of charity on behalf of the rest of humankind.

On that memorable night, I recalled the scenes I had experienced on a previous journey in service to the Lord alongside other coworkers, working for self-enlightenment and the construction of love amongst our incarnate brothers and sisters.

Taken by indefinable gratitude, I sought the repose I needed to meet the upcoming commitments I had been called to fulfill.

CHAPTER 2

A HIGHLY SIGNIFICANT SPIRITUAL ENDEAVOR

The day passed amid joyful and blessed expectations, and the hours went by smoothly in pleasant curiosity about the matter and work to which we would be called.

As evening descended uneventfully, mild breezes scented nature with the sweet fragrance of azaleas in bloom.

The stars twinkled in the night canopy, fraternizing with the bridal veil of Selene, and I beheld our beloved planet with lights glowing in the distance, representing its sanctuaries of love.

At the appointed time, I headed for the Communications Center, where the devoted brother Hildebrando was waiting with the charm of his kindly personality.

The small auditorium set up for the meeting was lovely. It was decorated with side garlands highlighting a stage decorated with tastefully arranged roses on the head table.

The place was soon filled with approximately one hundred guests.

Murmured conversations spoke of the pleasure of reunions, providing us a chance to talk about our activities, enriched with the joy of the work of self-enlightenment.

After a while, Aurelio, the director responsible for the Communications Center, entered the room. As an incarnate, he had been a devoted worker in the area of electrical engineering and had left an invaluable heritage for the benefit of society. At the moment, he was accompanied by a noble and venerable spirit radiating unparalleled kindness. His face was haloed by a charming smile and he displayed a significant magnetism that instantly filled all of us with affability.

We perceived his moral grandeur, in spite of his discretion and modesty.

Other counselors from the same department formed the fraternal entourage that led the visitor to the place of distinction at the head table.

The ensuing silence was natural as a penetrating harmony vibrated in the softly lit room.

A delicate fragrance filled the place and after a heartfelt prayer by Aurelio, the meeting began.

After a few introductory words, the venerable Aurelio informed us, without bombastic rhetoric or the usual but needless compliments, as is usually the case on the earth:

"It is my great pleasure to introduce brother Evandro, who has brought us a timely invitation of certain gravity.

"This benevolent friend has chosen our community for the implementation of a complex endeavor of assistance to a reputable institution dedicated to Jesus and patronized by the Cantor of God.[9] The institution is facing a dire threat by the Darkness...

"Without further ado, let us hear what brother Evandro has to say."

---

[9]   St. Francis of Assisi. – I.R.

The loving friend approached the podium and greeted us with an affable voice in the name of Jesus:

"You are well aware of the sensitive times in which our incarnate brothers and sisters are living, especially the Master's servants in the ranks of contemporary Spiritism.

"After the long night of persecutions and harsh trials endured by its apostles and pioneers, the movement is now expanding at an amazing pace, offering, especially in Brazil, the materialization of the loving Master's promise concerning the Comforter.

"Several factors have been in play so that the Kardecian message may find acceptance in various vehicles of dissemination by the mass media, and enjoy respect and consideration. These are highly significant times, for a good number of scientific authorities in various areas of thought do believe in the existence of God and the immortality of the spirit. Although their praiseworthy claims are suffering bombardment by atheism, the ones who are courageous enough to disclose their beliefs are not intimidated. A few winners of the Nobel Prize, for example, have affirmed that they believe in the Intelligent Causation of the universe and the reality of life after death...

"After they had penetrated the arcana of the micro-particles and the macrocosm, they came to the conclusion that there was no other rational explanation, except the reality of a Creator.

"At the same time, however, the wave of disrespect for life, and for ethical and moral principles, in addition to the overwhelming increase in the vulgarity of habits, is all supported by violence. A wave of madness is sweeping the orb, threatening its moral and spiritual structure.

"Aberrations are on the increase and the idols of illusion and absurdity attract hypnotized crowds who indulge in the strangest and most frightening behaviors.

"It is no wonder that hordes of low-order spirits intermingle with these misguided individuals and establish terrible and frightening obsessions that cause considerable sociological, psychological and moral harm to a numbed society that has lost the concept of accepted spiritual values."

The messenger of love paused for us to absorb his remarks, and then continued:

"The degradation of culture is alarming, and the worship of every sort of pleasure goes beyond anything that has ever happened in the course of history.

"Parents indulge in moral license with their children's playmates; many homes have become like brothels; and disrespect for the family sanctuary has reached high levels of cynicism and degradation that spill over into all sorts of criminality.

"Crazed authorities indulge in corruption while regular citizens wallow in poverty, without any hope or joy of living. Consequently they try to escape through the traps of depression, suicide and illegal drugs.

"I do not mean to sound overly pessimistic, but the moral situation of incarnate wayfarers is downright tragic. Of course there are exceptions, such as those who have used technology to reach for the stars, although their feet are still mired in the basest passions.

"It is at this time that Jesus' message, as unveiled by immortal spirits,[10] is being presented in its therapeutic and liberating character.

"Here is a great paradox: while more and more of the worldly are becoming fascinated by the illuminative Spiritist doctrine, many workers of that restored Gospel are slipping

---

[10] Reference to Spiritist works by spirit authors. – I.R.

into unfortunate behaviors, demonstrating their own moral fragility and the fact that they have not absorbed the Lord's sublime teachings, after all.

"Defections are continuous and personal downfalls are alarming to newcomers, who approach with innumerable expectations, anticipating support and guidance, especially through the power of personal example.

"Discarnates who exploit extreme fear in this sickly interaction use the mental space of these imprudent individuals to keep the sublime promises of Jesus from becoming fulfilled.

"When they cannot adversely affect the evangelistic activities of missionaries of the good and their living according to the truth, they seek out the distracted and boastful, the proud and self-sufficient to turn them into stumbling blocks, forming groups that fight each other, creating schisms and false scientific arguments that satisfy their vanity and disrupt the good progress of the healthy spread of the renewed faith.

"Unfortunately, the various currents, the offspring of disruption and pride, use hatred and slander to turn the arena of uplifting work into a destructive battlefield."

He paused again and I could perceive the emotion in his voice and the tears ready to fall. He continued:

"We have all rejoiced at the growth and acceptance of Spiritism by the masses. Nonetheless a natural peril threatens the harvest of the good. There are many who adhere to the Doctrine's postulates, but they are in no emotional shape to assume the responsibilities conferred on them by circumstances and by people lacking in common sense, thus giving rise to behavioral problems and difficulties that could otherwise be avoided. It is natural for many adherents of the message to be enthusiastic, to ardently become involved in its spread, and to live according to its liberating principles;

however, confrontations and challenges mixed in with personal problems do arise, and soon their joy fades and they make negative remarks about others, leading to conflicts if their suggestions or standards are not appreciated, suggestions which are frequently inspired by discarnate enemies of the Ideal, causing schisms, unhappy dissensions and defections in the flock.

"Worse still, they begin to have ideas that they believe are extremely important and they become tempted to correct, modify, or adapt to modern times the thought set forth in the Spiritist Codification itself, creating lines of thought that indulge in the frivolous or the social. Or they pretentiously claim that their idea is a step forward, a supplement to the Codification.

"This danger has already manifested and is growing like a fungus on the roots of a healthy plant. But if the fungus is pulled out, the plant is uprooted too.

"Measures need to be taken immediately to avoid what happened to nascent Christianity when it ascended the imperial throne of Rome and ousted Jesus; or what happened to Luther and his doctrine when others, claiming to be reformers, began adapting it to their own way of understanding the Gospel of love – which should be followed without excessive formalism or theological complexities – disguising their personal vanity and believing themselves to be founders of religions.

"This sort of struggle has gone on for a long, long time. It goes back to the very beginnings of thought, well-recorded in the biblical myth of Lucifer's rebellion against God.

"It follows that the lower passions predominant in the spirit during its intellectual and moral development do not surrender to the sublime achievements of love without great sacrifice and struggle.

"Right now, with the onset of moral anomalies of exorbitant pleasure, the sickly exchange between the hosts of evil and distracted human beings is winning continuous victories."

He paused once again so that we could grasp the seriousness of the situation, and then he continued:

"Of course the planetary transition is unstoppable, but it could at least entail less suffering which, unfortunately, is the current situation by human choice. The missionaries of love and knowledge who have been reincarnating, and others who will soon follow, need to find the human terrain already winnowed in order for the sublime endeavor to accelerate.

"In a certain way, we are all familiar with this sacrificial labor and we are fairly used to the demands of patience and persistent effort.

"The Saint of Assisi's former disciples from past days in Umbria have implored his help. They have reincarnated for the purpose of building a modern earthly institution dedicated to charity, without neglecting the simplicity of his loving heart. Deeply touched, he became a benefactor of the project and beseeched Jesus to bless it with success.

"Gradually, workers have been reincarnating and are coming together again, rebuilding the spiritual family whence they have come; a dawn of hope arising for the sufferers in the physical world. The project materialized under the light of the Comforter and has become a benchmark of dedication to Jesus on both planes of life.

"Devoted friends who have remained behind in our arena of action have begun to inspire and protect them, and to send selfless laborers to assist them. As the group grew, it began facing superlative difficulties, which have been overcome with Christian magnanimity, benefitting thousands of spirits.

"A center of labor for workers from our sphere, it has earned the seal of kindheartedness from the Master, who is aware of its spiritual significance.

"Multitudes are being benefited by its meritorious deeds, its doctrinal teachings, its evangelical service. The obsessed have recovered from spiritual persecution and are taking part in the labor of love; the depressed have gotten involved in the therapy of work, and the ignorant are being illuminated by the light of education.

"This has, of course, aroused great sympathy, but it has also inspired the animosities of jealousy, the unbridled competition of vanity, deliberate and bitter criticism, as well as patent and unbridled persecution. Nevertheless it endures like a well-guided ship in the storm, thanks to the mariners who command it with love and humility.

"Since it is included on the chart of the noble institutions contributing to the great planetary transition, it has attracted the attention of the Lord Jesus' traditional enemies, and they have decided to raze it once and for all.

"Because its members are united in faith and work, these enemies have been following them, waiting for any weakness that may arise so that they can enter the fortress and undermine it from within.

"And that is what has been slowly happening. The presumption and rudeness of one of its ambitious, childish, foolish and aggressive members has begun to take effect, generating unrest and becoming a moral breach for invasion by a lord of darkness, a wretched spirit who has been an enemy of Jesus since the end of the 15th century.[11]

---

[11] See chapter 19 and 20 (Confrontation with the Darkness) in our book *Planetary Transition* (LEAL Publisher, 2016). – Spirit Author.

"He personally took command of this imprudent member's mind, and we realize the gravity of the situation. Good workers have become aware of the danger and are seeking inspiration for immediate measures before irreversible damage is caused. They appealed through prayer to the Poverello[12] of God, who has assumed the overall command of the institution. He has called us to the delicate task of removing the obstacle by assisting this deranged spirit, since the Father does not want the death of the sinner, but rather that of the sin.

"A plan has been drawn up that includes all of you. You will go to various Spiritist Centers to assist the selfless servants of the Nazarene Messiah, whereas I and another small group will first attend to the nearly-foundering ship, and then proceed to other tasks.

"After this meeting, our brother Hildebrando will call out the names of our coworkers, and other teams will be formed to accompany us to the earth for the labor of love and protection to the beloved faithful servants of the truth.

"May the Lord bless our fraternal endeavor to help us serve Him as He has served all of us.

"Peace always in our lives with Jesus!"

When he returned to the table, sidereal harmonies permeated the auditorium and delicate petals of light fell on us, vanishing upon contact with our *bodies*, penetrating them with soothing energy.

We were all elated and engrossed in the contemplation of scenes appearing on a large screen above the stage.

It was a spectacle of the circus of Rome in the early days of the Christian faith, when the martyrs were thrown into the arena to die.

---

[12] St. Francis of Assisi – I.R.

Overcome, we could not hold back our tears and immense gratitude to those heroes of love and sanctification, who sacrificed themselves for the spread of the Gospel of Jesus during that harsh time.

The struggles had continued, though much milder, and now we were being invited to give ourselves to the unforgettable Rabbi.

There was no choice but to follow their example.

PLANNING SPIRITUAL ACTIVITIES

Hildebrando read a list of names to make up the respective teams, which would be meeting right afterwards in other rooms of the building to discuss plans for activities and the places where they would be carried out.

I was surprised and sincerely grateful to the Lord Jesus that my name was called. I presented myself at the proper spot with four other friends who had been Spiritists on the earth. I was already acquainted with them because they had allowed me to participate in their charitable endeavors, some of which I have narrated in previous books.

With great joy I embraced the venerable Jose Petitinga, a tireless worker for the Gospel. Kindly and gentle, he was overjoyed by our reunion. I was also reintroduced to the missionary Euripides Barsanulfo from Sacramento, Brazil. Euripides' captivating inner harmony infused me with balance and peace, briefly reminding me of our endeavors together in the not-too-distant past. I was also pleased that our little group included the Nazarene Master's wonderful servant, Jésus Gonçalves, a former Hansen's disease sufferer, whose evolutionary achievements over several reincarnations had provided him with moral excellence. Our group was complete with the addition of our supervisor and coordinator, the apostle Dr. Adolfo Bezerra de Menezes, and we headed for the room that had been reserved for us.

Upon arriving, Dr. Bezerra began projecting images on an immaculately white screen hanging on the back wall of the room, and explained to us:

"These scenes are being sent directly from the Spiritist institution that is one of the objects of our upcoming visit to the beloved planet."

He gave us some time to observe the spiritual activity of the place dedicated to spreading and living according to Spiritism.

It was an evening entailing a doctrinal study of the Spiritist Codification, and at that moment the speaker was just finishing up. We could see that he was inspired by the Center's mentor-spirit, as his listeners received appropriate bioenergetic aid.

The cameras that transmitted the images focused on the people exactly at the time of the closing prayer.

The attendees' fervor produced a high-potency vibration that was answered by a veritable shower of light particles that fell on and penetrated them while a number of spirit-benefactors assisted some of their loved ones by enveloping them in successive waves of soothing harmony.

There was a terribly depressed young woman who had been immersed in anguish while vampirized by a wicked, merciless discarnate enemy. But as she absorbed the highly subtle psychosphere, she seemed to awaken from her torpor and was overcome with tears, causing her desperation to vanish as if they had a cathartic effect on her misery. She recalled childhood scenes of suffering the loss of her mother and the subsequent abuse by her stepmother, which, combined with being obsessed by the discarnate persecutor, had triggered her psychological torment later on. As she evoked these memories, she recalled the mother with whom she had lived until she was just four.

Suddenly, her radiant mother approached and kissed her tenderly, whispering stimulating words of cheer and encouragement, which she captured intuitively.

One of the spirits in charge of the passes[13] in the large room began to apply the therapy needed to untangle her from the fluids of her enraged enemy, who sensed the failure of his intention of leading her to commit suicide. With that idea in her head, a devoted family member had taken her to the Spiritist Center, where she found out what would happen to her if she did kill herself. Upon contact with the energies saturated with strength and peace, the young woman's tears slowly diminished and in her head she could hear the voice of her selfless mother, who now found enough resonance to help her break free from her two-fold disorder: the psychological and the obsessive[14]...

When the lights were turned up – they had been dimmed for the final stage of the meeting – her cousin was surprised by her appearance. The young woman whispered to her timidly:

---

[13] "Passes are a transfusion of energy that alter the cellular field. ... In magnetic assistance, emission and reception are entwined, helping needy patients so that they can help themselves." (Andre Luiz, *In the Realms of Mediumship*, Ch. 17, International Spiritist Council, 2011). – I.R.

[14] The term "obsessive" from the Spiritist perspective, meaning persecution by her discarnate enemy. (See footnote 3 above). – I.R.

"I don't know what just happened. I can only say that I've been inundated with a sense of well-being that has been absent over the past few months. I had the feeling that my mother was here and that she was encouraging me. A strange thing happened, like I had just been disconnected from something that was constricting my chest and filling my head with constant thoughts of suicide... I was able to pray – something that I haven't been able to do for a long time."

She took hold of her cousin's hand in a gesture of gratitude, almost smiling, as her thrilled companion replied:

"Jesus has heard our prayers and you are being blessed with an opportunity to start over."

After a short pause, she concluded:

"Even so, this isn't a cure, but the first victory in the recovery process. Thanks to substances responsible for happiness and well-being, your meds will help you by rebalancing your neuro-communications. Meanwhile, Spiritist therapy will banish the discarnate adversary who has relished your depressive state, and who has been planning to snatch you from your body in order to continue his revenge... You'll win this battle using your own efforts and the blessings of heaven. Don't abandon the beneficial resource now at your fingertips. Stay vigilant because that spirit will try to return with even more power and defiance."

The young woman gave her cousin a hug and said to her:

"Please, help me in my weakness and don't let me succumb. I can feel the power of Jesus in my life... I need to beat this evil and go on living so I can be useful to myself and others."

Returning her spontaneous affection, her enlightened companion nodded and replied:

"I'll do all I can for you, but the hardest and most persistent part concerns you and your duties toward life..."

They left the room hand-in-hand, spiritually supported by the patient's mother.

We had all been following the incident with tears in our eyes.

We watched the other attendees as they left.

Two women were engaged in a lively conversation... Upon reaching the outer courtyard entryway, one of them said:

"There's no doubt about the beauty of our brother's message, but it was too long and a bit tiresome, and I must confess that I couldn't follow his line of thinking because I was watching the behavior of that wretched woman who had the gall to come to the meeting looking so disheveled ... Don't you think she might have some issues? She's looked so bedraggled lately and has been so quiet."

And as she was speaking such slander, she attracted an old discarnate accomplice who normally exploited her psychically, but who had been retained by the magnetic barriers[15] to the lecture hall...

The other woman, serene and gentle, replied:

"I disagree. I can't fathom how a 45-minute lecture so rich with optimism and such wonderful guidelines for our happiness could seem tiresome. In fact, I'm sorry it wasn't even longer, because I compared what he said with my own conduct and discovered certain emotional flaws that I will try to correct from now on.

"As for that woman, I heard that her husband discarnated in a tragic accident not even a month ago and that she has behaved with the dignity of a real Spiritist. Even though she's all torn up inside, she is bravely getting on with her life.

---

[15] These invisible barriers are installed by workers of the spirit world to keep out spirits who wish to disrupt and bring mayhem into the meetings. – I.R.

Of course she's sad, but I don't think she's as bedraggled as you describe her. It's just a matter of perspective... I see her as being deeply engrossed in what really matters in life, its surprises and how to handle them, overcoming the superficial worries that so often get all our attention."

The other woman felt discouraged in her nonsense but concluded her criticism:

"You always have an excuse for everything. That's your problem. You're too much of a Spiritist for my taste."

Her friend did not want to argue. She just smiled and said no more.

Other remarks enabled us to see how the message of the good resonates with listeners according to their interests and moral evolvement.

At that moment the speaker began to attend to the long line of troubled people who had come to the meeting to request his guidance and aid, his comfort and spiritual support.

Inspired by his mentor-spirit, he attended to each one kindly and cheerfully as the room emptied out.

The traffic of discarnates became heavier because in a little while there would be a special meeting to see to their various needs. Benevolent spirits pointed out the places to be occupied, while a soft melody echoing in the air surrounded the newcomers.

The music ended and Dr. Bezerra explained to us:

"That bustling institution will serve as our headquarters for the next thirty days, which we hope will be sufficient for our commitments.

"During this grave period of planetary transition to a world of regeneration,[16] suffering is increasing in intensity in human

---

[16] Categories of worlds regarding the "many dwellings in my Father's House": primitive, of trials and expiations, of regeneration, happy worlds, and

circles and spirits obstinate in evil realize they cannot continue their wicked exploits. Consequently, incensed and furious, they more ferociously attack those who become entangled in their snares, as if expecting to thwart the divine plans.

"The entire planet is enveloped in increasing difficulties, the natural result of thousands of years of human thoughtlessness and selfishness.

"People used to believe that military might could solve any difficulties between nations, but now the worst problems in every country are internal, resulting in innumerable disturbances that have caused unexpected harm to people who, unfortunately, have not yet awakened to true fraternity.

"Famine is decimating multitudes in an Africa in endless tribal warfare, while in many countries domestic revolutions are shaking those victimized by ruthless dictatorships. Fanatical religions are terrorizing; international finance is suffering the impact of administrative incompetence, and diseases of varied etiology are decimating bodies, minds and hearts.

"In a prophetic sermon, narrated in the 13th chapter of Mark, when Jesus refers to the great phenomena at the end of the immoral age, He states that if it were not because of the (Father's) elect, the suffering would be much, much worse.

"These elect are all those who have enabled themselves to be chosen by Him due to their conduct and their dedication to and respect for the sovereign laws.

"In this scenario of challenges and suffering, the Homeland of the Gospel[17] is also experiencing the damaging effects of social inequality, the suffering and abandonment

---

heavenly or divine worlds. See *The Gospel according to Spiritism*, Allan Kardec, Ch. III, Item 4. – I.R.

[17] A reference to Brazil. – I.R.

of minorities, the indifference of the powerful, absurd corruption, and the wrongful use of public resources that should be applied to benefit the people in need...

"Paternalistic and electioneering measures are being taken, but the causes of poverty are not being removed by educating the younger generations. Instead, they are being increasingly neglected in the forming of their character and regard for human rights through fair and duly enforced laws.

"The blessed domestic redoubt has lost its way and delusion has taken hold of almost every segment of society.

"Of course it is not for us to criticize these regrettable administrators, but to feel pity for them, since they will have to return to the terrestrial stage to collect the heaps of offenses they left behind, waiting for them. Clothed in suffering and deserving of compassion, perhaps they will expiate their wrongs on a world inferior to the earth they dishonored and assailed with their indifference and cruelty.

"As usual, the tools we will use in the activities designed by our mentors will always be those found in the Gospel of Jesus: love, kindness, compassion, hope, charity...

"We have not been chosen to reproach, complain or retaliate, but to understand and convey sympathy in every circumstance and condition.

"Many pitfalls await us; complex and embarrassing situations lie ahead. Even so, at all times the Lord will be sustaining us and inspiring us as to the best way.

"We will face very difficult moments during our endeavor. However, trusting in God, we shall not fall into the temptation to solve every problem, because we will know that the laws are fulfilled according to how they have been triggered by each person.

"In our work of disobsession,[18] let us have compassion on the suffering, but let us not forget the ones that are the unhappiest – those that are still dominated by prolonged hatred, without a moment of peace, having become downright criminals. As spiritual therapists for our discarnate brothers and sisters, compassion regarding their misfortune has to be a rule that keeps us from tuning in to their anger and cruelty. Even though Jesus was forceful when dealing with hateful spirits, He always had compassion on them.

"Thus one of the key ingredients of our excursion is assistance for the threatened institution and the new wayfarers in carnal attire, who have come from another dimension to take part in the great changes now taking place and increasing in speed and number.[19]

"Praying and letting ourselves be comforted by the song of the Beatitudes, we shall have the pleasure of fulfilling our commitment."

He paused, and benevolently asked brother Euripides to offer a prayer of gratitude to Jesus, which he did with unforgettable emotion. The next day we would meet at dusk and head for our generous mother, the beloved earth.

---

[18] Disobsession Therapy: Entails a dialogue to enlighten discarnate spirits who exert a harmful influence on incarnate individuals. For more in-depth information, please see paragraph 249 of *The Mediums' Book* by Allan Kardec. – I.R.

[19] See *Planetary Transition*, by Spirit Author Philomeno de Miranda (Leal Publisher, 2016). – I.R.

CHAPTER 4

BLESSED ACTIVITIES

As our team approached the noble earthly institution, nature was whispering the *Angelus,* reminding me of the native soil that had served as the birthplace for my last reincarnation. It was a bucolic spot in the state of Bahia, a small city inhabited by simple, fraternal people who cultivated the prevailing religious belief with respect and spiritual loftiness. That was always a time for silence and prayer, when the Blessed Mother of Jesus was invoked.

The memories took ahold of my entire being, and the sentiment of gratitude for total dedication to the Lord's service filled my heart.

In that moment of the rich, earthly spring, the sun gilded the white clouds floating in the heavenly canopy, presenting a spectacle of rare beauty in the changing of the colors that formed and modified the spectrum of light on the distant hills.

Even though the tumult of modern civilization was deafening, people were used to the circumstances of everyday life and were moving about automatically, looking for means of transportation in order to return to their homes.

We approached the spiritual redoubt that would serve as our base during our labors, and its blessed doors were wide open for whoever wanted to enter.

A laboratory of assistance and a sanctuary of love, it received a significant number of visitors from both planes of life – those in search of guidance and peace for the afflictions that undermined their moral and physical endurance – and they were assisted by dedicated servants committed to their duties.

The growing number of needy came for help at all hours, so the workers assisting them had made sure that, as a spiritual clinic, the Spiritist Center would be open from the early hours of the day until well into the night. After all, suffering does not have set times to manifest; it requires assistance whenever it may appear...

We were warmly received by the spirit-director, who had been cheerfully waiting for us. He introduced himself and explained that he had been associated with this group of workers ever since the remote days of St. Francis of Assisi at the dawn of his Holy Ministry. At that time, he had conducted himself badly as the head of a monastery, which, due to medieval ignorance and human presumption, had neglected its purpose to revive the Gospel of Jesus, yielding to pomp and distorting the thinking and attitudes of the *Troubadour of God.*

After a number of pain-filled rebirths, carrying the cross of remorse and sipping the gall of bitterness for their failure, that entire group of workers was now rediscovering Jesus in the Spiritist harvest field, based on the immortality of the spirit and the purpose of reviving His liberating Gospel.

His very name – Hermano – implied an invitation to the most authentic fraternity, to which he dedicated himself with joy and gratitude to God.

He invited us to enter the conference hall that we had seen earlier in our colony on the projection screen, and we made our way to the well-equipped room, located next to one reserved for mediumistic communications.

Having been informed beforehand about the program we would be involved in, Hermano and other benefactors of the Center had pledged to contribute to the success of the undertaking.

Thus, so that everything would be in order at the scheduled time, measures had been taken that would be compatible with the service to be rendered.

And since the room was a space reserved for serious, highly significant assistance, it had been carefully sterilized against the presence of mental vibrios or other morbific ideoplastic constructions so typical of collective environments.

Dr. Bezerra thanked his new friends for their benevolence and attention, and then excused himself to tell us we had two hours in which we could meditate and pray, or we could explore the building to familiarize ourselves with its fraternal services. However, at 8:00 p.m. we would all have to reconvene because that was when the work of assistance to hapless spirits from beyond the grave would begin. While the mediumistic ministry was in progress, the physically and spiritually infirm would be assisted in the conference hall through the study of a text from *The Gospel according to Spiritism* by Allan Kardec, and through the application of collective passes.

Personally, I felt I needed to prepare further, so I stayed where I was to ready myself for the important events.

I used those two hours to recall the endeavors of my last existence and to joyfully realize how spirit-benefactors work without humans even being aware of it. They do not expect any gratitude whatsoever, but work continuously for the good of others and the moral progress of society.

When such spiritual assistance becomes better understood in the conscious exchange of energies between the inhabitants of the two planes, incarnates will spare themselves many ills.

Hence I recalled the usefulness of mental control and uplifting ideas, while avoiding pessimism, complaining, and irritability. Through such lofty behavior the incarnate spirit frees itself from the cocoon of its misery and develops the ability to fly psychically toward the blissful regions that await us all someday.

I had not realized how quickly the time had passed, when everyone was back and we readied ourselves for our work.

Dr. Bezerra invited us to a prayer to Jesus to bless our upcoming endeavor and provide us with the proper conditions for the subsequent activities.

Very optimistic, he invited us to enter the large room to offer our special assistance to the illuminative session addressing those in need.

The lesson that evening addressed forgiveness as the primary condition for peace and health.

The lecturer recalled the Master blessing his enemies and aiding them with mercy. It was a plea to those present to free themselves from the morbus of resentment and its harmful vibrations...

Our attention was drawn to a young, very attractive woman, who was exuding dark, pestiferous energy deriving from her tormented thoughts and vices.

The *Doctor to the Poor*[20] approached her and asked us to observe her closely.

With the proper respect, we entered her mental landscape to help her and were able to observe the flow of her tormented thoughts.

---

[20] Dr. Bezerra de Menezes was known for his dedication to the poor. – I.R.

We saw that she worked as an escort catering to lonely gentlemen, that she made her living through the heinous trade of sex without commitment. At the same time, she depended on a professional exploiter who worked her to death, and to whom she surrendered in search of affection in her terrible loneliness...

She had often driven by this place on her way to "work." She had been attracted to its peaceful aspect and been touched and intrigued by the name on the door: Love and Charity Spiritist Society.

She had never given it further thought, but on that day, because she was distraught, she decided to find out about the place and seek information, which, through divine inspiration, culminated in motivating her to stay to listen to that night's comments and receive spiritual guidance afterward.

Relaxing from her chronic tension, she began to recall the past, which she had always avoided, considering that the memories only brought her grief.

She remembered the mother who had initiated her into an existence that was futile from infancy, because her mother transferred her own conflicts and aspirations to her in preparation for the parades of illusion.

A *human doll,* she was put on display everywhere as a child model, and as an adult she appeared on immoral TV shows that vie for glory and prizes, fame and money. She became famous and was fought over by gossip and sex magazines.

At age 16 she had already learned the art of deceit and the best exploitation techniques. She and her ever clever and ambitious mother got rich, which did promote them socially, but did not bring balance to their ever-exposed sentiments or fill their existential emptiness.

Her father had abandoned her at birth and after her mother discarnated, she was all alone. She became attached to worldly fantasies and lacked the psychological maturity to live a happy life.

When she realized that luxury and attention-getting were not bringing fulfillment, she began to harbor a great deal of resentment toward the mother who had pushed her into gilded but destructive experiences...

She envied the simple, hardworking, studious young women who aspired to build a better world by means of a loving family, whereas she herself was the envy of an immense legion of dreamy girls who had no idea about the dreadful price of fame and moral corruption.

She was now faced with a terrible dilemma and had come for help.

A medical examination had recently confirmed that changes in her body were due to her being pregnant...

She had come to feel some joy at the thought of the presence of a little one in her arms enriching her hours of loneliness. However, when she told her pimp, she had been cruelly rebuffed and accused:

"You've had sex with so many men, how do you know I'm its father?" he asked through clenched teeth.

Caught off guard, she explained that she always protected herself against pregnancy with all her other partners, but she had always given herself wholeheartedly to him in body and soul because she loved him...

Cynical and cruel, he struck back:

"You think we have a love relationship? You know I don't love anyone. I'm a professional; I don't feel anything special with anyone, no matter who. Sure, we see a lot of each other and we have spent some happy times together, but that doesn't mean I'm committed."

She felt like she had been stabbed in the heart, powerless, and could not even cry...

Moreover, he proposed:

"This is a recent development that will severely disrupt our business, so the best thing to do would be to get rid of it using a medically effective and safe procedure. You would have my full support. Otherwise..."

And he left, fuming with anger.

She was totally confused! She knew he exploited women, but she had thought that maybe with her it was different...

As a result of that jolt, she began to feel a great distaste for the idea of motherhood, for going ahead with the pregnancy.

She had come here expecting to receive supernatural help, because of the way immortality and Spiritism were presented...

She listened to the lecturer while thinking about an abortion.

Our mentor surprised us by informing us that the reincarnating spirit was the young woman's very own mother.

Upon awakening in the afterlife, she had been taken with anguish as she watched her daughter go down the dark corridors of moral self-destruction. She realized she was partly responsible and she hated herself for it. She was cruelly tormented by regret and guilt, and such feelings were drawing her to the young woman, seeing her so vulnerable and abandoned... Meanwhile she had also run into the ignominious discarnate enemy who was robbing her daughter of her vital energy, often making her feel burned out, exhausted, unable to see any meaning in life.

Now, faced with her exploiter's denial of paternity, the young woman was able to tune in to the vibrations of her mother anxious for forgiveness and the opportunity to make amends, although she emotionally harbored the criminal idea of abortion...

It was an unfortunate and very complex plot.

However, since no one is really alone or abandoned, her spirit guide was making every effort to help her, and just as she was passing by the Spiritist Center, he had inspired her to go in and get help, which made her change the course of her activities for that night.

Dr. Bezerra applied dispersive passes to her crown and brow chakras in order to disentangle the discarnate tormenter who was attached to her so ferociously. Next he put him to sleep with hypnotic induction and asked Euripides and Petitinga to take him to the mediumistic room, which they did with compassion and understanding.

Next, he asked Jésus to remain at the woman's side and watch over her, before taking her to the fraternal assistance department.[21] Then he and I headed for the disobsession meeting.

---

[21]   Most Spiritist Centers designate persons for a fraternal assistance dialogue with afflicted persons within the spiritual concepts of the Spiritist Doctrine. – I.R.

CHAPTER 5

LIBERATING PROCEDURES

The lecture was coming to an end and it was time for the collective passes, when the discarnate benefactors would apply wholesome energies to those in need.

As the sound system played a soft melody, qualified mediums took their positions in the aisles between the rows of seats, and while verbal and mental vibrations were emitted by the lecturer in a peaceful, well-modulated voice, beneficial energies were imparted to all those who were predisposed to receiving them.

Upon entering the mediumistic room, we found the work in full swing. Through psychophony,[22] two suffering spirits were expressing their anguish, the despair that had followed them after physical death. They were being caringly assisted through the psychotherapy of the Spiritist counselors'[23] enlightening words, while Hermano contributed simultaneously with his own vibrations.

---

[22] Oral spirit communications through a medium. – I.R.

[23] Qualified persons who dialogue with manifesting spirits in need of enlightenment. – I.R.

The two highly disciplined mediums were calmly externalizing the sufferings of the communicating spirits, enabling help to reach them effectively.

We could see that, as the counselors spoke fraternally with their thoughts set on Jesus, they exteriorized streams of silver-blue vibrations that reached the two recipients, soothing their moral wounds. The discarnate spirits could not explain the sensation of sudden comfort that had come over them. Fixated on disturbing memories and the effects of harmful actions from their past life retained in their perispirit,[24] they wallowed in torment, conveying details without enough lucidity to listen to counsel.

With remarkable patience, each counselor, assisted by spirit cooperators, used bioenergy to dissipate the heavy burden of afflictions, causing the visitors' anguish to diminish so they could receive verbal assistance.

Removed from the mediums and feeling much better than before, the two spirits entered into a hypnotic torpor and were placed on stretchers for later removal to a proper spirit colony for support.

Benefactor Hermano led the meeting composed of twenty incarnate brothers and sisters, including three psychophonic mediums, two psychographic[25] mediums, three counselors, two pass-givers[26] and ten other supporting members who mentally contributed part of the spiritual fluids necessary for the endeavor's success.

---

[24] Also known as the astral body. See *The Spirits' Book*, Allan Kardec, questions 93-95 (International Spiritist Council, 2nd edition) – I.R.

[25] Psychography: written communication by spirits through mediums. – I.R.

[26] See footnote #13 relating to "passes." – I.R.

Before the meeting Dr. Bezerra had asked Hermano for permission to assist the spirit-enemy of the tormented young woman who was in the adjacent room for the passes.

Thus as the spirit was brought in to communicate, the choice of medium fell on Celestina, a widowed mother of two children. She had raised them in the light of Spiritism and they too were now members of the Spiritist Center. She had earned the mentors' respect and affection because of her unparalleled dedication to working for the good, as well as her conscientious preparation as a medium.

As the ruthless avenger was taken to Celestina and came into contact with her perispirit, the magnetic connection took place instantaneously and Celestina trembled slightly. We noticed that some of her endocrine glands, especially the epiphysis,[27] displayed a peculiar luminosity that spread to the pituitary, the thyroid, and on down to the genesic (reproductive) center via the heart plexus, in a special circulatory system.

Automatically, the spirit began to speak through the medium, expressing exasperation and loathing at being there.

At first he wanted to harm the medium, externalizing waves of anger charged with destructive vibrations, which could affect her endocrine system and even her sympathetic nervous system. He was unsuccessful, however, because of her natural defenses.

Then he tried to free himself from the perispiritual magnetic connection that held him to the medium, culminating in his confronting the situation in an aggressive tone of voice:

"What do you want from me? Who dares stop my plan of revenge? What's going on?"

---

[27] The pineal gland. – I.R.

Strongly inspired by Dr. Bezerra, Marcelo, an experienced counselor, responded with kindness and clarity:

"My friend, we wanted to speak with you in order to examine your problem and the reasons for your suffering, now transformed into a cruel persecution of someone who obviously harmed you... We certainly do not want to stop you from pursuing your objective. We only want to understand why you are neglecting your own happiness by holding on to the rebellious attitude of hatred that makes you so unhappy. We also want to explain to you that, up to this point, you have acted as seemed best. But from now on, the possibilities of attacking this young woman have changed and you are being invited to alter your behavior for your own good."

And while the spirit ranted incoherently, Marcelo continued:

"Although your physical body has died, you may not be aware of the fact that there are universal laws of love, which no one can escape, thriving here in the spirit world. Nothing happens at anyone's whims... The sovereign laws work both automatically and by interference from the thoughts of those who direct their mind toward beseeching help and mercy. That is what is happening to both you and the young woman experiencing the thorns of your wickedness."

"Oh, you mean that dissolute and cruel life-destroying viper who's pretending to be an angel? She's callous and self-serving, a wrecker of homes and lives. She awakens passions, exploits her victims, and then hands herself over to a despicable accomplice who totally abuses her."

"You shouldn't talk like that about your victim, because, in your condition, your own energy is contributing greatly to her sickly behavior."

"Well, of course, it's only natural that it should be that way. I take pleasure in her debauched life. I take part in all her sexual trysts because they enable me to vampirize her energies. They nourish me."

"Do you think that's right? Since you criticize her way of life, how can you take advantage of her foolishness in order to enjoy benefits that are nothing more than madness and deadly emanations that degrade you even more?"

"It would be best if you minded your own business," he roared in exasperation, almost foaming with rage.

The medium's face was contorted, a perfect transfiguration reflecting the spirit's facial expressions.

Annoyed, shaking the medium, the infirm spirit screeched:

"Our relationship is lost in the hourglass of time, when this wretch, this tramp, betrayed me, already marked by her infamy. We were married and were loving parents – at least that's what I thought – when northern Portugal was invaded by French troops in 1808... After part of the invading army took up residence in our town, this wicked woman fell in love with a seductive soldier. It caused a major scandal, so she left home, which resulted in the death of one of our children, victimized by a cruel illness that had been eating away at his young body...

"Completely shameless, she moved to a different town, surrendering to the villain who had seduced her so easily.

"I succumbed to shame and horror, and I plunged into the abyss of hatred. I let myself be consumed by a strange sadness that wound up killing me, causing the death of our second child not long afterward...

"When I saw that there really is life after death, I went after her with a desperate feeling of revenge. I couldn't find her for a long time, but I was recently drawn to her current incarnation, so I knew she'd gone back... Our little one – the one that died prematurely – was now her mother, who left her to her fate. I don't know what happened to the other one, though."

He sobbed compulsively and then continued:

"An unwanted pregnancy would be the way for her to pay for her crime of abandonment. Due to her failure as a mother, it would help the child and her start anew, but I'm going to do my best to keep that from happening. I plan to bring her back here and get my revenge. Some of her other victims are also waiting for her and they're going to help me...

"If there are such things as law and justice, this is my statute of compensation. I don't want anything, except to make her pay for her past wrongs and the ones she's still doing to a lot of others."

When he paused, Marcelo, heavily inspired by Dr. Bezerra, explained:

"The divine laws are not applied as undue charges, but as mechanisms for rehabilitation and rebalancing.

"Of course the madness perpetrated by her is very serious, but that doesn't give you the right to extract justice, because yours is a capricious criterion full of resentment that is driving you to insane revenge. God doesn't need our help to make sure the laws of love are respected, and those who err receive corrective measures, which may entail purifying infirmities, the circumstances of life, relationship and affectivity problems, accidents, physical and mental impairments, and a host of effective methods for recovery. But those who seek revenge fall into the abyss of heinous crimes because they do not know the best way to correct the wrongdoer. So, they do not have the right to get revenge, no matter how victimized they may feel."

"But I hate her and I have to get revenge."

"Actually, what torments you isn't hatred, but your ignorance about the divine laws. The more you hold on to the poison of hatred, the more intoxicated you become with lasciviousness and perturbation. Consequently you get more attached to her, living almost completely in line with her moral transgressions. You're an exploiter dominated by a desire for perverse pleasure, dependent on the unhealthy behavior of your victim.

"It's time for you to change the focus of your aspirations so you can find happiness. After all, this whole period has been characterized by your seemingly endless suffering... The moment has dawned for you to throw off the shackles of your passions."

The venerable benefactor applied energies to the troubled spirit, while Marcelo continued:

"Step back in time and you'll see that there have been wrongs in your evolutionary spiritual economy, and that they rightly led to your suffering, which you could have used for your redemption if you had followed the guidelines of your religion at the time: forgiveness and mercy for that poor girl, just as Jesus forgave and had mercy on the woman caught in adultery."

As the psychotherapeutic induction continued, the obsessor began to squirm even more under the influence of the medium's spiritual fluids and, contemplating terrifying scenes, he began to cry out for help, succumbing before the archives of unhappy events that marked one of his latest existences.

"What I'm seeing just couldn't have happened to me!" he exclaimed, horrified.

"But it's exactly what happened, my brother. It's coming straight from the archives of your age-old memory. Your cruel deeds became a crop of misery for you to reap, but chauvinistic pride, a rebellious temperament and sickly selfishness kept you from assimilating your suffering, leaving your son to discarnate because of neglect. You complain that your wife left home, and you blame her for the deaths of your two children, but, drowning in bitterness, you too forgot to offer them the support they needed after she had gone... One cannot lift the hammer of justice against others, since one also has terrible debts that continue to create deplorable situations.

"Take a good look at your past madness, the perverse arrogance that marked your life, and stop playing the victim. Think about others for a change, those who experienced your wickedness, who became victims of your indifference and cruelty."

In deep concentration, Marcelo perceived the images evoked by the obsessor's memory due to the past life regression technique employed by Dr. Bezerra.

After a few minutes, the exhausted obsessor asked:

"Well, what's going to happen to me now?"

"God's love knows no boundaries," responded Marcelo, the spirit-psychotherapist. "You will be sent to a spirit community as a patient to receive appropriate treatment, renewing yourself and adapting to new behavior. And you will let our poor sister proceed according to the Law of Cause and Effect.

"Now rest and sleep in peace so you can wake up in another dimension and in a different state than the one you've been in for almost two hundred years."

He applied calming energies to the medium, reaching the spirit and putting him fast asleep. Subsequently he was disconnected from the medium, put on a stretcher and taken to the proper place for later removal.

Celestina regained lucidity, haloed by vibrations of harmony, enjoying excellent mental and emotional balance.

Dr. Bezerra was overjoyed with the first phase of our work of assistance. He invited us to follow him to the room where, at that moment, the young woman was reaching out for guidance from the earlier presenter.

There were several other sufferers patiently waiting their turn. They were being called in order by a coworker who used a list prepared beforehand.

The visitor felt emotionally overtaken by a strange sense of well-being she had not felt in a long time. She did not know she had been released from the unhealthy constriction of her persecutor. She was not even aware of the fact that she had been obsessed.

She immediately sat down to be assisted and began to breathe the psychosphere exteriorized by Jesus' servant, who welcomed her with obvious kindness, quite different from what she was used to.

He let her talk, and she disclosed her drama, especially the desire to have an abortion, but without explaining her conduct.

During the narrative she was moved by a feeling of self-pity for the first time in a long time. She felt a mild tremor, as if she were an inexperienced teenager, as was the case when it came to good and true fraternity.

The kindly attendant listened and then explained the gravity of the crime of abortion. He asked her to think long and hard about it before making a decision. The fact that the father did not want to take responsibility was not important, because her love could fill the gap left by his absence.

As he explained the *miracle of life*, immortality and reincarnation to her, he did it with compassion and fraternity, enveloping her in soothing harmony.

At the same time, Dr. Bezerra applied special energies and when the assistance ended, the young woman promised she would return.

She left quite moved, and as she got in the car she decided to go back to her apartment but not go back to "work." She immediately called saying that she could not see the next client on her schedule because she had suddenly become ill.

Aware of her happy decision, our noble mentor explained to us that she would soon be brought back to the institution partially disengaged from her body during sleep.

CHAPTER 6

THE ASSISTANCE CONTINUES

We realized at that moment that those events had not resulted from mere chance, but from the assistance of a noble spirit who loved her.

He introduced himself to us, explaining that he had been a French soldier who had deceived her during the conquest of Iberia by Napoleon's troops.

Later, when old age had given him a deeper understanding about life, he acknowledged the wrong he had committed against her, for, after he had kept her for some time, he left her and returned to his homeland without the least bit of compassion, set on starting a family. The memory of her, however, was fixed in his mind and emotions for the rest of his physical existence.

Old and overwhelmed by guilt, he sought to right the wrong he had done by doing what good he could do. Moreover, in the afterlife he had undergone a radical transformation after he had found her in a dreadful situation in a region of unhappiness, from which he could not rescue her.

Both had returned to the earth afterward under different conditions. He had reincarnated on the banks of the Loire and Cher rivers in Tour, France, and became familiar with Spiritism – after Allan Kardec's discarnation. There he met the apostle Léon Denis[28] and participated in numerous meetings with the eminent writer, born in the village of Foug in the vicinity of Toul, and discarnated in that city of Honoré de Balzac...

Significantly transformed, when he returned to the homeland of spirits in the early 20th century, with his consciousness awakened to the good, he sought to rehabilitate himself of his former misdeeds by committing himself to uplifting the one whom he had deceived and whose family he had caused so much misery.

During his last existence, he had been called Philippe. He had kept a low profile and had used every means possible to help his former victim, seeking to keep her off the slope of error and wrongdoings...

He was a member of the team that worked at the Love and Charity Spiritist Center, and when he found out about our upcoming activities, he had requested Dr. Bezerra's help and guidance, culminating in the assistance to the spiritually sick girl.

Kindly and aware of his responsibilities, Philippe joined our team in matters concerning caring for the young Martina...

I reflected in silence, seeking to understand the divine designs, which always find ingenious resources for solving the problems created by human ignorance and shortsightedness.

Up to this point I had not thought about who might be responsible for helping the misguided young woman who had suddenly decided to enter the institution she had passed by several times before, without giving it a second thought.

---

[28] Léon Denis (1846-1927) was a notable Spiritist philosopher, and with Gabriel Delanne and Camille Flammarion, one of the principal exponents of Spiritism after the death of Allan Kardec. https://en.wikipedia.org. – I.R.

The complexity of that endeavor fit a carefully prepared plan, whose goal was liberation.

We returned to the mediumistic room, where we observed other communications by tormented spirits. We continued to learn the techniques of compassion and mercy that were applied there instead of useless discussions full of pompous, empty words that did not meet the dramas and appeals of the suffering.

The Spiritist therapy offered to despairing discarnates is different from anything applied to incarnate patients. The situation of both is very different, in that all the ailments of the former are imprinted on the perispirit, which records actions and their effects, requiring generous vibrations of love and charity in order to be diluted through new emotional patterns. Of course words do assist in the treatment of afflictions, but they are more effective when filled with compassion and fraternal understanding, with no reprimands or pretentious demands on the one they are meant to educate, persuade and change... The goal is to comfort rather than dominate the minds and sentiments of discarnate patients.

However, when argumentative and recalcitrant spirits are present – as in this case – besides the sentiment of pity toward their ignorance, one should avoid fruitless discussions that impair the endeavor, because they steal time from charitable activities and spend it on empty debates of human vanity. Hence, such attempts at persuasion should be halted and the communication ended, leaving higher order spirits in charge of instructing them after the *animic shock*[29] – one of

---

[29] "Animic" in Spiritism refers to psychic phenomena derived from the incarnate spirit itself. In Spiritist mediumistic sessions, the expression "animic shock" refers to the contact effected between the perispirit of a discarnate spirit and the perispirit of an incarnate medium. It represents

the basic purposes of the therapeutic device – resulting from the communication.

During this *animic shock,* the spirit transfers to the medium the heavy load of deleterious fluids that engulf and dishearten it. The spirit, in turn, is renewed by spiritual fluids externalized by the medium, benefiting immediately. And due to his or her tranquility and emotional balance, the medium can easily eliminate such sickly energies through sweating and other bodily mechanisms. Even if no verbal counseling is involved – which in other instances is necessary, if not indispensable – the mere fact that this mediumistic contact has occurred means that the discarnate is already in a proper condition for assimilating a significant share of healthy energy.

In a confrontation with perverse obsessors who are aware of the evils they do, the goal is still to help them without criticizing them or creating worse conflicts.

Jesus is the model in every single situation. Whenever He attended to the obsessed, He always took pity on their spirit-persecutors,[30] and after He *expelled them,* He counted on the assistance of His spirit-assistants to enlighten them. In His time and in the circumstances in which the obsessed appeared, the curative act had to be immediate, without delay, in order to demonstrate to that *spiritually ignorant generation* the power with which He was vested. Thus it was much different from the providential mechanisms in use nowadays in the mediumistic sanctuaries built by Spiritism.

---

one of the possible therapies for needy and perturbed discarnate spirits. The medium in this case, in a serene mental state, normally in prayer, will be the agent of a "shock" of good emotional vibrations that will contribute to the recovery of the perturbed spirit's equilibrium. – I.R.

[30] Referred to as "unclean spirits" in the Gospel. – I.R.

The lovely work of illumination entered the final phase as several cases of obsession and spiritual ignorance were attended to.

Then Hermano offered the closing prayer, drawing on inspiration which he conveyed to Marcelo as director of the work. In the dimly lit room, members took a small dose of energized water and then went to another room in silence.

I stayed busy with the other workers, helping to move those who had been assisted and who now needed to be taken to the spirit community, whereas others who could not be helped were sent to wards in the institution itself. All was done in a climate of order and respect, as all spiritual activities ought to be. Also, special equipment was used to purify the room of the heavier fluids adhering to the walls and ceiling or remaining in the psychosphere so that future activities would not suffer unhealthy contamination.

Vibrations of harmony hovered in the air, plucked on delicate harps by invisible hands.

Dr. Bezerra advised us to renew our energies either by joining nature in its starry festival or by praying, until the moment when an activity would be especially dedicated to Martina, who would be brought, partially disengaged during sleep, to that bastion of love.

Without a doubt, Spiritism had come to earth with the mission to restore the immaculate doctrine of Jesus.

Stripped of the vestments of the superstitions and external worship forms that clothed the *mysteries* or doctrines of knowledge that had originated in ancient India, passing on to Egypt and its sanctuaries of initiations, then fascinating the Greeks and synthesized in the music of Orpheus and the poetry of Homer before reaching its culmination in Pythagoras, Socrates and Plato, it was

Jesus who best summed up the universal wisdom in the incomparable hymn of love.

Corrupted by the passions that prevailed at the core of their being, people back then were unable to grasp the excellence of His teaching, desecrating its content and adulterating it...

When science finally rent the veil of ignorance and provided a better understanding of life and its *miracles,* the profound teachings returned in the voice of the spirits, the true songbooks of immortality, repeating the age-old lessons about the reality of the immortal being outside the physical vessel, about reincarnation, and about the effort required in order to break free from the heavy cloak of illusion that holds the individual on the lower levels of evolution.

There, in the simplicity of that temple of love, we observed the greatness of God's love for His creatures, providing everyone opportunities for moral growth and happiness.

No protectionism, no neglecting anyone, whoever he or she might be. The most impoverished, at times ostracized, are creditors of care and opportunity, and the most affluent also face the same criteria of the laws of merit that foster the skillful mechanisms of evolution.

The Center's wall clock indicated 1:30 a.m. when we gathered in the mediumistic room. Partially disengaged from their physical bodies through sleep, Celestina, Marcelo and a small group of co-workers, assisted by Hermano, were already there, along with members of our team.

Philippe entered, carefully leading the sleeping Martina, also partially disengaged.

When the members of the mediumistic endeavor had taken their places at the table, the patient was placed in a comfortable chair near the director of the meeting.

Dr. Bezerra approached the physically beautiful young woman and gently brought her to consciousness.

Finding herself in the strange room, she gazed at the spirits present and asked: "I think I must be in dreamland; am I?"

"You might put it like that, my child," answered the benevolent guide. "Actually, you are in the land of reality, where we are all born and live, whence we travel to earth for a learning experience, and whither we return afterward."

She smiled, somewhat awkwardly and let herself be infused by the ambient vibrations.

Then her former mother, in the process of reincarnating as her future child, was brought to Martina, who squirmed and wanted to move away. But she was restrained by our brother Petitinga, who gently told her to stay put.

"It's a ghost. My mother's dead."

"That's right!" said the spirit friend. "And she is here in order to make amends."

"What about all the terrible things she did to me? I hate her now that I understand the abyss I was thrown into by her and her guidance on beauty and seduction."

The woman was visibly moved and began crying softly when she heard her desperate daughter's aggressive response.

"She admits she was wrong," he continued, "and she wants to make it right – which everyone is entitled to do, including you. This very day you have received a magnificent favor from Heaven, blessing you with love and assistance, both indispensable for being happy."

"I don't get any of this... I'm confused about what's been happening lately and I just don't know what to do."

"All you have to do is open the door to the sentiment of love and let it come in; bless her with forgiveness. She did harm you but thought she was helping you, according to sickly earthly ways."

Petitinga's kind and gentle words had an impact on the confused girl.

"What can she possibly want from me? She's already harmed me badly enough. What else does she want from me?"

Meanwhile, Dr. Bezerra gave the discarnate mother a subtle signal. Embarrassed but grasping the significance of the moment, the woman said:

"Forgive me, my child. I lived only for you. Now I know how much harm I caused you, sending you down the path of illusion and vulgarity... I was ignorant of spiritual truths, so I tried to give you what I thought was best. Then, after death, I found life and witnessed your gilded, illusory torment.

"I would never hurt you – I love you too much.

"You were little and frail, and you needed support and opportunity to be successful in the world. So I made myself your tutor and sent you down the road to money and power... But how wrong I was!

"I want to make it up to you and correct my terrible wrong. Please, don't expel me."

The request was made in an indefinable tone of voice interwoven with anguish and hope.

The young woman was overcome with shock and stood up, demanding:

"Expel you from where?"

"Your womb. I must return to your arms and your warm lap to rest a while and then take care of you in the harsh days of the future."

"No. I won't allow it. I've suffered too much and now I'm rich and famous. I have no desire to take on new risks. I don't know what I'm going to do. I'm really upset with what's been happening in my life all of a sudden.

"There are lots of reasons why I need to get an abortion. Mainly, there's no one to help me out while pregnant; plus I don't want to ruin my figure while I can still save up money. After all, youth is a liqueur that is sipped too quickly."

"Oh, have mercy on your mother and accept me!"

"Oh, God!" the girl exclaimed. "I must be crazy. This is some kind of nightmare."

The kindly Petitinga stroked her head and explained:

"No, you're not crazy, and this isn't a nightmare. You're facing the reality of life. Seize the moment for long awaited happiness. Everything can be explained and, little by little, you will understand what has been happening in your life of late.

"Look who's here."

Philippe approached, smiling, lightly haloed by an adamantine light:

"Maria Jose, do you remember me?" he asked, gently.

She looked at him in surprise and let out a squeal, asking:

"Marcel, where have you been all this time?"

"Seeking enough light and wisdom to beg your forgiveness. Time hasn't kept us apart. On the contrary, it has united us, and I'm back, not as the reckless soldier that caused you so much harm by leaving you, but as the love of your life, eager for care and affection."

They embraced, filled with emotion.

Sobbing, Martina moaned and wailed:

"My God! I just don't get any of this! What a mixed up dream; yet I'm so happy."

"Rest assured, beloved of my heart. I've been looking for you for almost two centuries, and now that I've found you, I'm never going to leave.

"Can you forgive me for running off at the wrong time? I went out to conquer the infinite in order to offer you peace at this time."

"I've always loved you, even in those stormy days of abandonment, loneliness, illness and death. Of course I forgive you."

"Then forgive your dear mother too. She is the little boy you left to die when you ran away with me. Now she's back... Nothing is lost in life. Everything balances out."

"I have no idea what you're talking about."

"Don't worry about it for now. Just forgive her, and forget the desire to end your pregnancy. That way, you'll be redeeming yourself for having abandoned her, that child in your past life, so that she too may set herself free from guilt for your ills. Everything has its reason for being. There is a law of cause and effect in the universe and nothing happens without its seal."

"For you, I'll do anything," she agreed breathlessly.

They embraced again, and then, somewhat awkwardly she hugged her mother in tears of pain.

Dr. Bezerra treated her with vigorous passes and explained:

"You will have very difficult moments in light of your decision, and people will try to talk you out of it. You will need to take refuge in prayer and seek shelter in this house of love. All of us here will be at your side whenever you need us.

"Now rest and get some sleep."

At a sign from the Benefactor, Philippe took her back home.

CHAPTER 7

LOVE NEVER SETS LIMITS

At that moment, two of the spirits who helped out at the Spiritist Center's usual mediumship meetings entered, carrying one of its directors, partially disengaged from the physical body, asleep on a stretcher.

It was Anacleto, who was just over fifty years old. He had been widowed about five years ago. Before that, he had been a dedicated Servant of the Gospel, and had been one of the institution's pillars of strength.

According to what I could deduce mentally from the thoughts emitted by Dr. Bezerra, Anacleto had imprudently begun to cultivate self-glorifying ideas and aggressive behavior. He had become a prickly thorn in the work group.

Responsible for highly important activities, he had been sexually reserved while married. But after the discarnation of his wife – also a dedicated Spiritist worker – he had begun to cultivate disturbing sentiments and dormant tendencies. He let his imagination run wild, generating toxic mental pictures that were slowly absorbed and transformed into mental habits.

He had gradually let lust get the best of him during the difficult period of andropause and had become unruly and overbearing.

He would provoke his coworkers with vulgar words for any reason whatsoever. He abandoned principled conduct and began frequenting "love" motels with equally disturbed young women with loose morals.

He had become narcissistic and had disconnected emotionally from his spiritual duties. He would take part in the meetings with no inner commitment, showing disinterest in his position as director. Consequently his work at the Spiritist Center suffered, and although the board members needed solid rapport amongst themselves, he would react rudely, if not crassly when called upon to cooperate with the group.

He had even reached the point of embezzling the Center's funds in order to support his tormented desires.

His discarnate wife was understandably distressed at observing the excesses of her wayward consort, so she resorted to Dr. Bezerra and requested immediate help. Dr. Bezerra, in turn, made a request of *God's Troubadour*, who took the measures now materializing in our team in order to prevent worse damage to Anacleto and the Center.

His most serious problem was his delusion about his personal power, such that he felt he did not have to answer to his coworkers for his administrative acts, nor accept any interference or fraternal attitude that might modify the situation.

Several attempts at dialogue were rebuffed with shocking behavior, and he would show total disrespect toward all who approached him.

Things had come to a head, and his friends were about to call a general meeting to remove him from the administrative picture. This would undoubtedly cause a scandal as Anacleto would undoubtedly be unhappy about it and react irrationally, further complicating and adversely affecting the Center's concept as a place dedicated to love and charity.

He was brought into the room, snoring loudly, showing the conflicts that afflicted him, and tossing and turning, as if wanting to free himself of some uncomfortable constriction.

I observed him more closely and saw that he was being strongly subjected to a very serious obsession by several ovoid forms,[31] reminding me of the medusa of Greek mythology. The "hair" consisted of a number of these spirit-beings fluttering around his head and emitting strange, wild animal-like noises.

They were spirits, victims of monoideism, which had been imposed on them through perverse hypnological processes crafted by a skillful enemy of the good, who deemed himself in charge of a veritable legion of discarnates suffering his cruel dictates.

Furthering my observation, I saw that two more ovoids were affixed to Anacleto's central nervous system, two to his reproductive organs, and one to his crown chakra, in a case of very serious, exploitative parasitosis.

These deformed, deranged spirits were so strongly attached that previous attempts to disconnect them from the patient had failed, so he was brought here now for spiritual help.

His reproductive area was dominated by veritable *vibrios* created by his moral dissolution, threatening his physiological organization, subjected to his disturbed mind.

It was only natural that his thoughts were so morally unbalanced, because his brain was suffering the insidious

---

[31] For an explanation of ovoid forms, see the book *Liberation,* Ch. 7 "A Painful Sight," by the Spirit Andre Luiz, psychographed by Francisco Candido Xavier (International Spiritist Council, 2013). – I.R.

presence of the ovoid controlling his upper brain region, drenching it with harmful energies.

His central nervous system, in turn, suffered interference from the pathetic spiritual mind that was feeding on his energetic tonus, draining him slowly but surely.

It was obvious that, if such conditions were to persist much longer, a continued stable existence would become impossible. Some consuming illness would certainly take advantage of the lack of resistance of his equally compromised immune system, further decimating his already broken body. At the same time, his behavior would induce insanity, with unpredictable consequences, were it not for the therapeutic measures to which he was about to be submitted.

The repercussions of a scandal, a physical assault or something more disastrous would be terrible for the group of apprehensive and distressed servants of Jesus.

Anacleto was undoubtedly the victim of a ruthless obsession under distant but well-directed control.

His physical appearance indicated a state of malnutrition and lack of energy due to the sapping of his vitality.

In the natural silence of the room wrapped in soothing harmonious vibrations, Dr. Bezerra prayed for Jesus' help for the activity that was about to start, pleading for His blessings on behalf of all those who were involved in this bleak picture of obsession: the victim as well as his tormentors.

A diaphanous light filled the room as heaven's response to the appeal from earth.

The spirit-doctor approached Anacleto and, focusing on his reproductive area, inhabited by the two deformed entities, he began to apply a special type of energy in a counterclockwise motion, as if unscrewing each ovoid's tentacle attached to the gonads.

These tentacles had something like suction cups – resembling those of an octopus – with a powerful ability to attach externally to an organ and absorb its contents.

All of us were in deep concentration, directing our thought as an active force on behalf of the procedure.

The dedicated benefactor worked at the liberating process for more than five minutes until the two fluidic tubes that fed the entities were disconnected.

The noble surgeon and Petitinga, who functioned as his direct assistant, carefully grasped the fluttering ovoid forms.

The two degenerate beings emitted strange noises. Their perispirits had been altered and were in a condition of deterioration, the spurious fruit of their behavior in past lives, culminating with their falling into the traps set by the vile hypnotizer now manipulating them.

They were immediately placed within the auras of Celestina and another medium, both in deep concentration.

Upon connecting energetically with the two disciplined mediums, they began to stir, moving continuously, jerking occasionally, and making animal sounds that indicated untold suffering because they were unable to manifest it verbally.

As they received energy emitted from the hands of Hermano, Petitinga and Jésus in transcendent and soothing contact, Dr. Bezerra spoke gently to them:

"The liberation you require has begun, although it will still take some time. It is necessary to recover your lost form by utilizing the perispiritual envelope of the mediums who have become your intermediaries, so that, in a pain-filled future reincarnation, you can return to your former state, which you used improperly.

"You have endured this radical transformation for many years, but the time has come to return to a normal life.

All the patrimony you have stored up over time, and which is now archived in the core of your being, will slowly return and you will be able to advance down the path of progress.

"Jesus always goes in search of His lost sheep, and you, my brothers, are a perfect example of the recalcitrant spirits who have fallen into the depths of the abyss where you now find yourselves.

"Since you are able to think – even though you cannot speak – turn to God and beg for His mercy. The days of horror and misfortune are about to give way to a period of hope and joy of living."

As he spoke and conveyed healthy energies to the deformed spirits, we picked up on the despair they were expressing through their thoughts, in spite of the monoideism that had degenerated their perispiritual form, keeping them in that deplorable situation.

Those mental messages were full of despair, madness, anxiety and anguish.

Returning to articulated speech so that they could hear him through the mediumistic faculty of the selfless mediums, Dr. Bezerra informed them:

"You will be taken to hospital facilities in the spirit world. There, you will be treated appropriately to prepare you for reincarnation on earth, where the blessing of expiation will restore your lost harmony.

"Never forget love, and remember that a wrong is a shadow that indelibly accompanies those who commit it.

"Our Father's love, however, has no dimensions or borders. It is the driving force of the universe. Let yourselves be flooded with that sublime energy and you will easily achieve peace. Even if it may seem that your complete liberation is taking a very long time, it will end in victory. You have been mired in evil and have practiced it for a long time, particularly in the aberrations practiced in the insane pursuit of irresponsible and criminal sensory pleasure.

"So calm down and let yourselves be led by the Lord's mercy, without protesting the suffering that you have imposed on yourselves."

The mediums' oscillations and small convulsions slowly decreased as the ovoids became disconnected from the generous spiritual fluids in which they were immersed.

Next they were placed on a stretcher prepared beforehand and taken to the proper place in the room, from where they would be taken to the hospital for an extensive period of care.

Dr. Bezerra immediately returned to Anacleto, who was still asleep and groaning, victim of the ongoing constriction by the remaining discarnate enemies. He then repeated the very same procedure on the two ovoids that were affixed to Anacleto's central nervous system at the rear base of the brain, at the point where the spine begins.

The entities seemed to grasp what was going on because, as they fluttered in the air, they seemed highly agitated, as if insisting on maintaining the vampiric situation.

Imperturbable and conscientious, the surgeon of love and charity continued his procedure for a while longer until he was able to remove them as he had the first two, inducing them to communicate through the two mediums in concentration – the essential condition for the success of the undertaking.

When their agitation grew worse and more anguished, Dr. Bezerra said to them:

"Nothing remains as our whims would have it, because life has a sublime purpose. And even when human beings have bound themselves to wrongdoing, they are granted a redemptive opportunity. The Father's compassion for His wayward children surpasses anything that the human mind can imagine. So the time has come for both of you to face the consequences of your own negligence so that you may awaken to pressing, new realities.

"Fruitlessly, evil will remain on earth, but its course, no matter how long it may seem, will always be short-lived, for only the good is permanent because it comes from God.

"Under the allure of your tormenter, you are still rebelling for having lost the energetic exploitation of this poor misguided man's energy, without realizing that regardless of their condition, everyone deserves mercy and compassion. Our concern at the moment is you, dear brothers, since you have endured this awful, degrading deformation for too long.

"Right now, the best thing for you to do is to abandon the idea of revenge, as well as the criminal pleasure that transformed you into degenerates before the divine laws."

During the inevitable pause, I perceived their revolt and indignation, which were quite different from those of the first two ovoids.

Dr. Bezerra continued:

"It is impossible for the darkness to resist the light and for hate to oppose love. The victory shall always belong to the Eternal Good.

"Now go to sleep and rest a while, given the madness consuming you. A new day and opportunity will dawn as an unexpected blessing for your future happiness.

"Be at peace, for no one can forever escape their destiny, the plenitude that all will enjoy someday.

"God bless you, dear brothers!"

The procedure followed for the first two ovoids was repeated for these two.

With that task taken care of, Dr. Bezerra approached Anacleto and roused him with soft and gentle words.

Visibly dazed, and with a congested look on his face, he asked:

"Is this a court of law? What's the charge?"

Dr. Bezerra calmly replied:

"No, my friend, you are in our sanctuary of love and charity. The court you have referred to is your own conscience, where God's law is written. Conflicts of conduct have led your heavy conscience to fear the divine justice because of your infractions against duties that you freely assumed."

This timely response calmed him down and he realized he was outside his physical body and in the Spiritist Center where he himself was a director.

As he became aware and recognized the venerable figure directing the endeavor, as well as the presence of our small group of spirit workers, he broke down in tears of despair, complaining:

"The darkness took hold of me. I have been forsaken by my guides, I, who have been so very faithful to them for so long."

"Now don't assume the role of martyr or the victim of abandonment," said the loving mentor, "when you know perfectly well that you yourself are responsible for your many misbehaviors and for the danger you have brought to this venerable institution as a result of your irresponsibility and moral insanity."

His voice was stern, necessary for awakening the trickster who was pretending he had been forgotten by Providence.

Dr. Bezerra went on to explain:

"We are taking steps to minimize the damage caused by your loss of composure and to call your attention to your responsibilities so you can change your behavior and thus free yourself from the darkness that has indeed enveloped you, with your full consent.

"Where is your responsibility toward your work for Jesus and the steadfastness of your faith if you let yourself go down the thorny path of insanity and become an instrument of disruption and disaster for an endeavor that is a pillar of support for the spread of Spiritism on the earth?

"You cannot play with the issues of the immortal spirit or abandon your responsibilities without suffering the consequences. So change the focus of your thoughts and let's talk."

As the patient awakened emotionally and psychically to assess the follies he had been committing, he was overcome with natural tears of repentance, expressing a real desire to regain his peace.

Lucidly facing the reality, he listened as the good guide explained:

"From this moment on, although you are still attuned to the malevolent spirits to whom you willingly surrendered, you will receive our help so that you may be released from their pernicious influence and find your way again.

"Prayer and moral discipline in positive and continuous reflection shall comprise your guidelines of security, keeping you vigilant regarding the exploits of unhealthy, harmful pleasure.

"Regain the lost way and go forward with inner harmony on the redemptive path alongside your friends and coworkers, without becoming an abyss or impediment to our achieving our lofty spiritual goals.

"Now, rest and preserve the memory of this unforgettable moment.

"A new opportunity is dawning and you must use it wisely.

"God bless you!"

Enveloped in tenderness and harmony, Anacleto fell asleep in peace, without convulsions, and was taken back home by Jésus and another assistant of the mediumistic activity.

CHAPTER 8

DELVING INTO UNDERSTANDINGS

During the natural break in our work, Dr. Bezerra explained:

"Someone will probably wonder why we didn't free our brother from the ovoid entity connected to his crown chakra.

"Let me say that it was a healthy, preventive measure in terms of reestablishing his balance.

"When individuals experience the malevolent influence of spirits of that level, their psychophysical organization remains intoxicated by the poisonous fluids they inbreathe and they adapt to the sickly circumstances. If it is suddenly released from the unhealthy tonus, it suffers a collapse of the mind-body interaction and the patient may experience memory loss, hallucinations or emotional dystonia.

"Thus recovery must occur slowly enough to enable the body to adapt to the new intake of now-healthy energies that will eliminate the sequelae left by the destructive toxins.

"Our brother will wake up nauseated and in a bad mood, with only vague memories of our meeting, but with a serious interest in changing his mental and moral conduct.

"The path of vice is long and tortuous, causing much damage to all those who irresponsibly tread it in their hunger for harmful pleasures.

"True health begins with dignifying thoughts that build strong psychical combatants that are always on alert and ready to fight the viruses produced by enemies of the good. These viruses invade the cellular organization of careless individuals, sustaining them in the unwholesome desires in which they find pleasure.

"Prayer and edifying thoughts create specific antiviruses that protect against harmful contamination.

"It is always well-advised to maintain the mental balance from which emanate the energies compatible with the vibratory field elected for the existential experience."

He was silent for a little while and then continued:

"We are serving Jesus, and it is only natural that all those who make themselves His enemies for whatever reason see us as enemies too, because we are an impediment to their plans of expansion and victory.

"Our brother Anacleto has been a victim of his own imprudence for not having resisted and overcome the impulses to which his spiritual faith was submitted. Since he wasn't prepared for widowhood and loneliness, he opened up mental space for musings, the first step to giving access to all kinds of torments, resulting in his being besieged by the minions of Rabbi Eliachim ben Saddoch,[32] whom we remember so well... When the rabbi was unmasked in a past meeting with the messengers of the Lord, he vowed to fight the new Christians, as he was already doing, but now, in his conceit, investing

---

[32] See *Planetary Transition*, also by Spirit Author Philomeno de Miranda (LEAL Publisher, 2016). – I.R.

everything within his power to prevent the winning of hearts by the Kardecian doctrine...

"Thus he went looking for several institutions dedicated to the practice of, and living according to, Spiritism. And to proceed with his fierce battle, he chose this one because of its excellent Christian agenda and its connection with the Poverello of Assisi, stigmatizing it and leading it into scandals damaging to the doctrine.

"His accursed plan was perceived by Hermano and the spirit workers who run the Center. They resorted to St. Francis — as we already know — and measures of love are being applied.

"As soon as the wretched rabbi becomes aware of what is happening at the moment, he will rise up with his evil hosts in a massive assault against all who toil here, especially the one who has given him an emotional opening...

"Therefore we must be vigilant and humble, and surrender to Jesus, the Great Care-Taker of the Harvest, so that He may lead us with His wisdom, and that the confrontations that await us may transpire in a climate of charity, never departing from the guidelines of the good and compassion."

The venerable apostle had tears in his eyes. His voice was soft and sweet, but deep and full of meaning.

He continued:

"Of course, the institution's mediums, directors and other members will, in the coming days, be harassed by thugs in the service of their ignoble leader. Traps will be set; assaults will be part of the plan for vengeance, as well as clashes within families and at work. It will be a violent siege, such that some will desert or surrender to rebelliousness and unwarranted questions, like: Since I am doing the good, why is evil persecuting me? Where are the spiritual defenses on my behalf?

"Over a long period of time, everyone has received training and knowledge about what occurs outside the curtain of flesh with regard to the interaction between the two vibrational dimensions in which incarnates and discarnates reside so that the training and knowledge can be applied at the appropriate time... And now, that significant moment in our lives has arrived. So, there is no reason for doubt and inner conflicts, which only open gaps in one's moral armor to contemptible suggestions by the enemies of Jesus...

"During this time of the great planetary transition, many terrifying phenomena are occurring and will continue to occur. They are the rotten fruit of people's increasingly depraved social conduct, but they will attract people's attention to the change that will provide harmony and true joy of living.

"No one is excused from cooperating for a better world, because the laws are fulfilled with or without the consent of humans, and even in spite of their lack of cooperation.

"The terrestrial ship sails its course in the sidereal ocean, suffering some stormy injunctions. But let us not forget that Jesus is at the helm."

Next, due to the dominant harmonious vibrations in the environment, a few more suffering spirits were attended to by receiving explanations about their conditions and the appropriate therapy for their recovery.

At 3:00 a.m. the endeavor ended and the incarnate participants went home, supported by the devoted workers of the Cause.

The next day we went to visit Anacleto and observe his awakening marked by a singular emotional indisposition and fragmented memories of what had happened the previous day.

He understood that he had experienced a lucid out-of-body experience, during which he was benefited by mentors from the Spiritist Center. At this point his own commitments to the Center came back to his memory. He was able to take stock and come to grips with his lapse in behavior, repenting sincerely...

In that mental climate, it occurred to him to pray sincerely for Heaven's continued support. He was immediately answered by Dr. Bezerra, who began inspiring him more deeply, mitigating the insidious fluidic interference of the ovoid entity magnetized to his crown center, and causing the mental numbness dominating him...

He felt renewed, as if he were reviving after a foggy period. He prepared for the day's activities and thought about meeting with friends that evening, opening his heart to them and telling them about his torments. He would apologize and promise to tighten ranks with them.

He even smiled at the anticipation of returning, aware of his spiritual duties like in the past.

When we returned to our Center of activities we observed that, around the institution, as had happened on other occasions involving struggles between the forces of Christ and the wicked opponents of the Light, veritable assault troops were arming for a siege. They were attempting to isolate it from the surrounding buildings to prevent help from coming from outside...

In their ignorance and presumptuousness, they assumed they knew what they actually did not know, taking measures compatible with earthly strategies.

It looked like they were preparing for a traditional battle, where the invading forces surround the impregnable and challenging fortress, thinking it will be an easy victory.

A number of spirits wearing rabbinical garb and bearing horrible scowls were using chain leashes to control and restrain ferocious beings victimized by zoanthropy, depicting wolfish and canine features.

Ancient tuba-like instruments emitted strange sounds from time to time, and powerful voices, amplified with the help of special devices, repeated orders in Hebrew and shouted war slogans, like in the past during battles against the enemies of Israel.

The surrounding environment became pernicious due the low-level vibrations of the *troops*. Spears cut through the air now and then, thrown against the Center and those who had come there for help.

A number of the more sensitive patients displayed sudden discomfort or a strange, painful sensation in their body when struck, but they quickly recovered upon entering the beneficent Center's conference and collective passes room.

Denoting responsibility and seriousness, Dr. Bezerra – and the rest of us with him – unnoticed to the attackers, traversed the barriers being erected in a construction of pernicious fluids, and called director Hermano for a meeting.

Always at our mentor's side, we perceived the significance of the moment, and with thoughts fixed on Jesus and His love for all of us, we met in the mediumship room with the spirit responsible for the institution and with those in charge of its multiple tasks.

After a quiet moment of reflection, Dr. Bezerra began:

"As expected, our brother Rabbi has taken the measures that he deemed best for the confrontation.

"Believing himself great in his smallness, he is commanding the troops with which he insanely plans to besiege this stronghold of faith and cause damage to the living persons and us, the discarnates, who meet here. The stupidity of his presumption has armed him with a combatant behavior that is no longer compatible to our field of action, especially since he discarnated more than four centuries ago...

"Indeed the fragile minds of many of this Center's attendees will attune to the morbific waves emitted with the force of resentment and hatred, promoting disturbing reciprocity for themselves.

"As for us, as we face this challenge, the only alternative is compassion – the daughter of love – combined with a spirit of solidarity and support, winning the violent forces over to the hosts of peace.

"In their upcoming doctrinal lectures, it would be appropriate for the doctrinal disseminators to explain the difficulties that appear periodically on everybody's pathway, which also happens in mediumistic communications, so that everyone may become aware of this time of struggles. By extension, prayer and good deeds should be applied as precautionary and inhibitive measures against the force of evil from our midst. Thus, inspired by the spirit-mentors, who are also aware of the responsibilities that concern us all, an emotional and fluidic environment of security and balance will be created during the upcoming struggle.

"The final battle will be one of love, extinguishing the flames of hatred in those who fan them with their ignorance and stubbornness.

"May the Lord of blessings bless and keep us in His designs of peace!"

The spiritual activities at the Spiritist Center continued without interruption throughout the day, but as evening approached, during the time preceding the giving of passes to troubled visitors, something happened that gave us an indication of the gravity of the moment.

The room was full and the presenter was preparing to start the study of *The Gospel according to Spiritism,* when shouting and quarreling were heard at the entrance gate.

The culprit was a man known in the neighborhood, who was afflicted by profound mental disorders. Telementalized by one of the chief besiegers, he had approached the institution for the first time, under the control of two spirit obsessors, demanding entrance.

Individuals in charge of security gently tried to dissuade him and take him to another area, but he meant to disrupt the meeting and cause a riot. He had become physically violent and foul-mouthed, wanting to know where the so-often touted charity and love were.

The four male workers who were futilely struggling to keep him out and guide him to a small room off to the side. Almost getting into a physical altercation, they were the target of mockery, jeers and infamies shouted by the mob of spirits, urging the four to continue and challenging them to physical combat, frightening the attendees and causing panic...

Hermano went to take care of the problem, and praying sincerely, he approached the mentally disturbed man and touched his forehead, discharging special energies that disconnected the two fierce obsessors, who withdrew after experiencing a type of strong vibratory shock...

The poor man, who had lost a great deal of energy while in the painful grasp of the obsessors, grew weak and almost fainted. He was supported by the four incarnate assistants, who finally managed to carry him to the adjacent room, where he received loving care.

Some of the visitors, not realizing what was happening, had got up out of their seats and had tried to get involved in the unpleasant incident, but were prevented by the lecturer, who, referring to the mental patient with tenderness and mercy, informed them that everything was under control.

The meeting began with a moving prayer inspired by Hermano. Then the text *Without Charity There Is No Salvation*[33] was read, generating a psychosphere of great peace and spiritual comfort.

We were overjoyed to see Martina amongst those present. She was holding a copy of the book of consolation and hope, visibly changed, without too much make-up and with her hair modestly tied back.

Her eyes shone as she listened to the enlightening words of the speaker.

When the lecture was over, the healing mediums took their places, and as prayers were being said on behalf of the absent, the sick, the discarnate, the afflicted and the needy, passes for liberation from harmful fluids were applied in a climate of true solidarity.

That was how the early Christians proceeded in the catacombs and humble venues, evoking the protection of Jesus.

Later, the study groups would meet, and new attempts at aggression were certainly foreseen, for violence is stubborn and madness knows no bounds.

We joyfully waited for night to fall, having won the victory in the first round of the terrible fray.

---

[33] From *The Gospel according to Spiritism*, by Allan Kardec. – I.R.

THE GREAT CHALLENGE

Undoubtedly, for the world to be transformed, human beings must change for the better as each one is a *mater unit* of society. As long as the planet's inhabitants refuse their inner transformation and hold on to their spiritual infirmity – the result of their evolutionary backwardness – no external force will ever change the planet's moral progress.

The times in which we are living are times of self-enlightening effort, thanks to revelations that are descending to the earth more frequently, in addition to reliable information regarding the process of change, offering a vision of the future that lies ahead for all of us.

For over two thousand years, the lessons of the Master of Nazareth have called us to upright moral conduct, peaceful coexistence and compliance with the duties of solidarity and support for those still in the rearguard of ignorance, or those suffering the phenomena of renewal through pain, trial or afflictive experiences...

All must be prepared to accompany the march of progress, integrating into the legion of builders of a new era for humanity.

Thanks to the phenomena of the law of ethical and moral development, this efficient endeavor is occurring in many segments of society, which knows nothing about spiritual reality. Spiritists, however, should be the ones making the greatest contribution to renewal because they are well-informed regarding events imposed by divine law, which can no longer be postponed. This period of transition, announced by Jesus and referred to by John the Evangelist in the Book of Revelation, and spoken of by prophets throughout history, is now being fulfilled according to the divine plan which has laid the regenerative destiny of the benevolent earth, without the pungent and hopeless marks of suffering.

The forces of evil, however, insist on maintaining the current picture of desolation, alongside abuses of all kinds, because they intend to continue to psychically exploit unwary individuals who are linked to them by the unwholesome habits they enjoy in the illusion of matter.

Nevertheless death inevitably comes to all, and when they awaken in the afterlife, they are crushed by reality. They rue their wrongs and long for an opportunity to make amends. However this will not take place on the earth – which will cease to be a planet of trials and expiations – but on one of a lower evolutionary state,[34] where they will expunge their evil and moral bankruptcy in a situation that is much more afflictive and bitter.

Mediumship in the service of Jesus has been an invaluable tool so that reliable information about life and immortality may awaken those who sleep or who refuse to understand the phenomenon of the great change. They will be swept away by the force of exile, which will take them

---

[34] See footnote 17. – I.R.

to another inescapable dimension to learn to respect the sovereign laws.

We were meditating on this premise during the minutes prior to the public meeting dedicated to the study of Spiritism through a program of well-prepared topics aimed at understanding the Doctrine and assimilating its invaluable liberating resources.

We were all in the room, observing the start of the lecture by the Gospel's devoted servant, whose life was a rosary of ennobling deeds.

After his prayer, and as he was preparing to speak, we heard a thud and saw that a tormented woman had fallen out of her chair and, in a fit of hysteria, had begun screaming.

A perverse spirit connected to her was constricting her genital glands and hitting her in the womb, producing an indescribable sensation of despair. At the same time, it held her in a rudimentary process of mediumistic trance.

The unexpected fall and the unusual fit of hysteria in that room dedicated to people's lofty spiritualization caused understandable discomfort in the audience.

Kindly but impulsive onlookers rushed noisily to help the woman up, though they had no skills for such an effort.

There was, unavoidably, some unnecessary panic, but trained members approached the woman and applied passes while speaking softly to her spirit persecutor, who was under the mental control of one of the combatant rabbis outside.

A neuropath, as well as inexperienced in mediumistic communications, the woman was visiting the Center for the first time, and there, along with her organic problem, she had allowed her obsessor to take her over in a trance-like state.

Dr. Bezerra also approached her and conversed sternly with the spirit, the agent of the unfortunate spectacle, counseling him properly and leading him away from the troubled woman.

The soothing passes had calmed her down. Feeling somewhat bewildered, she was helped back to her seat by the watchful assistants.

In the meantime, the shouting outside recalled the savagery of primitive beings, while their weapons struck the institution's defenses without causing any harm.

Suddenly, amplifying the loud and disruptive noise of the tubas, I heard the strange echo of an unfamiliar instrument, which produced a significant amount of discomfort due the vibratory charge it emitted.

Petitinga said to me:

"That's the sound of the *shofar*, a loudly-blown ram's horn the Hebrews used long ago during battles and religious ceremonies.

"During worship it is sounded after the reading from the Torah. It is considered one of the oldest wind instruments known, and can have various meanings, depending on the tones sounded on it. The one sounding right now symbolizes threat, time to engage the enemy."

With that event, the tormenters of peace hoped to generate disharmony and fear in the environment, which would enable the mob to enter and cause various disruptions. Even though the incarnates could neither see nor hear what was going on in the spirit world, they did experience sensations resulting from the aggressiveness of the persecutors if they happened to be attuned to the perverse maneuvers contaminating the psychosphere and creating embarrassing situations. For example, the unhealthy influence would induce the mentally ill, family members and maladjusted individuals to act aggressively or disrespectfully toward those who were there for illuminating experiences.

Fortunately, measures were immediately taken to restore balance, cancelling the possibility of an invasion.

Dr. Bezerra was concerned and conveyed it to Hermano and the rest of our team:

"We need to strengthen the defenses.

"Let us focus on Jesus and ask Him to assist us with a phalanx of operators from our sphere."

The presentation continued, as did the audience's attention.

Our work group and the Center's spirit-director continued to concentrate, praying fervently with absolute faith in the Incomparable Master.

Suddenly, a powerful light descended and filled the whole environment. Within it were a number of spirits that had been male while incarnated. Wearing beautiful medieval garb, they were accompanied by others in less formal attire. They introduced themselves to Dr. Bezerra as specialists in buildings and defenses.

"They are a group of mentalizers skilled in constructing buildings," the head of our group informed us. "Some of them belong to the ancient order of the Knights Templar who are still dedicated to the aid of those who suffer and are defenders of all those who have given themselves to Jesus. They are advised by modern engineers who specialize in *constructions* as we have them in our spiritual spheres."

They all smiled cheerfully and began their work, which entailed a number of them concentrating mentally, causing material to appear from the *cosmic fluid*. Others used this material to construct a large rectangular building, whose base sat in the conference room.

At the same time, sidereal voices sang a moving melody of exaltation to the Lord of Life.

Little by little, a building was being raised that was reminiscent of the old watchtowers of medieval castles. The work was completed in less than an hour. It was higher than the physical building, and was fitted with devices that resembled small-caliber cannons capable of emitting magnetic rays that produced unpleasant shocks when they hit their target.

The group worked efficiently and harmoniously, and when the lecturer ended the presentation and was about ready to close with prayer, the commander informed us that they were prepared for the confrontation.

Radiating great joy, the audience was preparing to leave, while the afflicted woman was invited to remain in the room in order to receive expert guidance for her problem...

We went up to the highest part of the building, from where we could watch the huge crowd of feral discarnates. At a signal from the spirit responsible for the defenses, rays were fired at the mob, which fell back, cursing infernally, threatening and screaming...

The head of the operation explained to us:

"For this level of spirits, the most effective resource is still the one that will frighten and intimidate them. Afterwards, specific arrangements will be made to assist the entire group."

Before we could ask about the possible damage that the discharges could cause their perispirits, he captured our thought and answered with a friendly smile:

"It is more of an instrument of intimidation than one that can cause real harm.

"When the rays hit them, they produce an unpleasant feeling like a light electric shock. However, when it comes to the more complex problems entailing the menacing evil of the darkness, we are justified in increasing the power to cause more discomfort.

"Love has resources of varied application, which always depends on the needs of the receiver."

The would-be invaders had scattered and were now at some distance away, thinking more about themselves and no longer interested in the individuals leaving the Center.

More rays were fired from time to time to keep the invaders at bay. We were able to see the dark, viscous circle of their mental exteriorizations around the illuminated area containing the sanctuary of charity.

Dr. Bezerra was touched and thanked the diligent group for their cooperation, asking the leader:

"Do you have any further instructions?"

"Yes," he responded kindly, "we need to inform you that the director of operations has decided that we should stay here and offer assistance until the spiritual cleansing work is finished."

The benefactor joyfully embraced him and we returned to the room. It was almost deserted, except for the afflicted woman, who was receiving instructions from one of the Center's mediums strongly inspired by her spirit guide.

The angelic melody still hung in the air, pouring out spiritual harmonies...

If the forces of evil devise and execute plans in their wickedness and insanity, love has powerful countermeasures that are able to cancel out their ill effects.

As we pondered the wisdom of high-order spirits, their dignified methods, and mercy toward offenders, we were overcome with increasing emotion and commitment to devoting as much time as possible in charity toward our neighbor, which, ultimately, meant charity toward ourselves.

ENCOUNTER WITH THE DARKNESS

The hours passed in a state of calm as the night progressed.

In the middle of the night, while the Center's members were asleep, diligent workers from our sphere went to a number of homes to lead invited members back to the Center for a special meeting soon to begin.

Besides the two mediums and Spiritist counselors that have already introduced, the group also included our brother Anacleto, who had triggered the serious ongoing process.

The sleeping members were trickling in. They were aroused and informed about the plan established for that time.

At 2:00 a.m. we were all occupying our positions, much as would occur during normal mediumistic activity at any Spiritist Center, when Dr. Bezerra explained to us:

"I think that we will soon be joined by Rabbi Eliachim ben Saddoch, who by now is well-informed about our institution's defenses.

"Feeling that he has been attacked, he will soon appear at the head of his troops to challenge us to a confrontation using the weapons of evil and destruction that he is familiar with..."

He had not even finished the sentence when we heard a screechy voice coming from outside, amplified by a special apparatus, inviting our mentor to come out and face the consequences of his act of retaliation against the *Forces of the Salvation of Mankind*, as they called themselves, ironically...

The racket was deafening. Desperate voices were mingled with tribal instruments, including the continuous sound of the *shofar*, just as occurred in remote times of battle, causing the Hebrews' enemies to panic...

The shrill voice with a heavy Hebrew accent repeated the invitation, which culminated with swearing and threats, and emphasizing the word *cowards*, associated with the meekness of Jesus.

We listened to the entire provocation. Dr. Bezerra remained calm and concentrated, not showing any reaction.

"Your own courage and that of your minions," shouted the challenger, "are only expressed through betrayal and use of the barbaric and infamous methods of the Inquisition."

Offensive laughter erupted and mockery rained down from all over.

Radiating vibrations of compassion extending beyond the room and toward the offender, Dr. Bezerra remained apparently unaffected by the challenge.

In the meantime, the stentorian voice proclaimed:

"If the lamb doesn't face the challenge, the wolf will come and devour the flock..."

There was sudden silence, followed by orders and strange sounds similar to ancient war chariots advancing into battle.

Dr. Bezerra asked us to concentrate deeply. He amplified our sight and we were able to see a veritable army of strange beings advancing in battle formation.

He mentally asked Hermano to hold off on the defenses at the entryway. As the *troops* of the offense advanced, at the rear, in a ridiculously constructed chariot – somewhat ghostly and military at the same time – was the Rabbi surrounded by a few of his most eminent commanders.

His strategy was for a large number of his warriors to penetrate the defenses, after which he and his chiefs would enter the battle with all their ferocity, as if they were still on the earth – such was their complete delusion.

The first group entered the conference hall, followed by the Rabbi's cortege.

At that moment, Dr. Bezerra gave Hermano the order to close off the entryway and reinforce the defenses, while the watchtower's cannons fired off a large quantity of darts that forced the rest of the invaders to retreat.

The important thing was that this time the Rabbi was inside the institution's defenses with his best combatants.

We noticed significant activity amongst the spirit workers.

They approached the room's boundaries in an orderly manner and quietly pushed on them as if they were composed of modules, expanding the area such that several rooms were transformed into one very large hall filled with attackers in all their wild fury, while we servants of the good stood opposite the entrance in concentration and harmony.

The attackers exuded morbid emanations consisting of a foul odor like unburied corpses.

Dogs, wolves and various beasts guarded the attacking group, while enraged commanders shouted disconnected orders in total emotional chaos.

Right after what we might call the suicide battalion at the front came the Rabbi and his chiefs. They too were emotionally imbalanced and dressed in regalia, as if they were in an ancient battle of their people, mixing together religious and bellicose customs.

They were enveloped by the thick and menacing dark cloud resulting from the psychical emanations of the raving mob, which then reabsorbed it, becoming even more intoxicated.

As the cannons continued firing warning shots at the invaders, the rebel shouted angrily:

"Once again we have fallen into a trap set by the miserable followers of the Lamb, just as has always happened throughout history. Let's get out of here right now."

There was a rout in all directions, but no means of escape. The defenses were reinforced not only by defensive energies, but by a large number of Templars dressed in the manner of days past and in a guardian position around the hall.

They raised their hands, emitting vibrations of love and, in a hymn of praise to Christ Jesus they began to sing an exhortation of compassion and mercy.

A shower of rain drops of light illuminated by lofty spiritual fluids immediately began falling on the rebels, calming them down little by little.

The din subsided, and as if anesthetized by the sublime energies, they dropped their grotesque, primitive weapons and fell to the ground. A few were overcome with emotions of peace and began sobbing, while others remained silent and stupefied, almost insensitive, but calm...

Soon, the only thing standing out was the strange apparatus carrying the Rabbi and his commanders. He was ranting, feeling betrayed and beleaguered, as if he were an outcast and not the religious authority that attributed to himself qualities that he did not actually have.

Dr. Bezerra, haloed by a soft spiritual light that indicated his condition as a true apostle of Jesus, approached the furious invader and invited him to a fraternal dialogue.

"Why should I talk with the enemy? I came here to fight, not talk. My aim is to wipe out the infamous destroyers of the Jewish faith. They see themselves as possessors of the truth, having as their Messiah a vagabond who threatened the hegemony of the Roman Empire and the doctrine of Moses, and who was justly crucified as the thief that he was."

Our dazed visitor's perispirit showed significant deformations and his red eyes emitted deadly rays of powerful energy typical of the evil featured in demonic allegories.

As he spoke, he radiated dark waves that dissipated on contact with the continuous rain of luminous spiritual fluids filling the place.

Dr. Bezerra did not react negatively, but responded:

"I am not the one who is going to parley with you, my friend, for I am fully aware of my own smallness and lack of merit for what is a highly significant time for many of us.

"Let us wait for a more authoritative voice, one that will come to us on behalf of Him whom you so vehemently reject."

The surrounding light intensified, and the magnificent spirit of Francis of Assisi descended to our group, dressed in a humble medieval habit and radiating a special luminosity.

He was escorted by some of his former companions. Together they constituted a small cortege of high-order spirits whom Jesus' love had sent to those gloomy surroundings characterized by wretches crushed by suffering grief disguised as madness and a yearning for revenge.

As the Apostle of Poverty reached our group, exclamations of joy, surprise and unexpected excitement arose from all sides.

Some of the Rabbi's companions retreated, timid and frightened, while he himself remained in his place, adamant and proud. The space between him and us had been transformed into a veritable arena.

Preserving the distance that was automatically established, the sublime visitor stretched forth his hands accustomed to charity and mercy, and with an unforgettable voice, he said to the Rabbi:

"May the Lord be praised in all things, including the suffering and despair of those who are unfortunate, and especially for those who deny Him!

"The doctrine that human beings have followed is not His, but one of human passions. He, who blessed the cross of shame, rendering it the angelic wings of liberation, would never agree with any attitude that would damage His postulates of indiscriminate love, especially for us Gentiles, because His own people did not want, receive or accept Him.

"To demonstrate His mercy He offered His helping hands to the woman living in error, the adulteress condemned by the law, and the lepers of body and soul. He even met with members of the Sanhedrin, who came to Him in the silence of the night, as well as the powerful of the world, who needed Him.

"Without a trace of vainglory He became the way of redemption for all who have had enough of the world and its illusions, supporting them with tenderness and affection.

"And to you also, brother Rabbi, He is offering His hands marked by the nails of the cross – applied by the Sanhedrin, which imposed it on the Roman ruler – praying for forgiveness for those who martyred Him in the times of ignorance in the distant past.

"Not measuring distances, nor fearing the wrongful reaction of earthly rulers, He is above all governments and presumptuous authorities. He asks that all evolve toward Him, for He is waiting for us with a light burden and an easy yoke.

"This is the moment of liberation sounding for you, dear brother, as you have been deceived by human pride and the mistaken notion that you are a ruler, although unable to master your own passions.

"Postponing this opportunity would be to write a painful chapter in your unfortunate experience for many centuries to come.

"Even brother wolf and sister birds yielded to His voice when I had the chance to encounter them. So, it will not be you, brother Rabbi, knower of the spiritual laws – someone who thinks and loves – who will refuse to receive Him right now."

He was about to continue his sublime invitation, when the bizarre sounds increased and the inclement invader lashed out, swearing.

Taken with compassion, with no resentment toward the aggressor, God's Poverello replied:

"I understand your pain because I also once found myself faced with the alternative: God or the world! My own father told the bishop of the city that I was a demented, rebellious and spendthrift son who was always causing him financial harm because I had sided with the poor... At that decisive moment, like a flash, I heard Jesus asking, 'Who are my father, my mother and my brothers, but those who do God's will?' and I decided to be His lesser brother.

"I renounced wealth and my father's support, stripping myself of everything that belonged to him, and donned a robe taken from the trash...

"Whatever belongs to the world remains in the world. Whatever follows us after death is what belongs to God and what comes from Him.

"So, do not kick against the goads and hold on to the perverse attitudes of those who mistreated you, deluded by the lying world. They were false representatives of Jesus."

The Rabbi roared in despair and hatred, contorting in moral pain and from the memories of the fire that had consumed his body in the now distant 15th century.

"I will never forget," he thundered, foaming with rage, "I will never forgive, even if I wind up being consumed in the eternal flames of Hell. I hate that troublemaker Jesus and His minions. I have sided with the forces of revenge during my long exile in Hades and I promised myself I would stand against those who plan to bring Him back. We prefer the world as it is, with its wickedness and cruelties, its unrest and passion for pleasure.

"So, don't come to me with your whimpering, talking to me about humility and detachment. I don't know what they mean. Time has been a great friend. It has enabled me to manipulate the minds that nourish me and my companions, who cherish my inspiring them to leave behind their bewildering poverty, suffering and misery...

"The powerful, avenging God of Israel is my model and it was He who determined my behavior to submit to my whip and ferocity the wretched Gentiles, who have been excluded from His election ever since the Creation..."

Taken with great compassion, noble Francis interrupted him:

"What a cruel error in reasoning supports your sickly thought! How could the earth, so rich in gifts and beauty, in this universe of harmony, have been created for the misery of the loftiest beings that live on it?! How could the divine Fatherhood be destructive, since He is the Cause of all this?! Could anyone believe that Perfection could produce degeneration and misfortune, and elect a tiny group as His descendants, discarding the rest of humanity that does not know Him, yet is not to blame for its ignorance?!

"The Father, whom Jesus brought us, is all love and mercy, whereas the rebelliousness that proceeds from the still-developing human mind has been the cause of the suffering that will lead it to grasp the meaning of life and the sovereign codes of balance and order.

"Despite our differences of opinion, we are brothers; we have come from the same Divine Womb and we are advancing toward a meeting with truth. And that will make us happy."

These words were spoken with infinite kindness and they echoed around the room as a special melody of love, sensitizing the receptive listeners and calming down the overly excited.

The tubas had gone silent, but now and then we could hear the terrible sound of the *shofar*.

In desperation, the suffering Rabbi retorted:

"That is all just nonsense. Here I am, besieged and betrayed yet again after having fallen into the vile trap set for me. I came here to fight. I did not come here to be imprisoned and made to change my mind by your forces of oppression.

"I demand the doors be opened so that I can return to the battlefield with my followers!"

Serenely, the *Sun of Assisi*, recalling what Jesus would do in similar circumstances, explained:

"In your situation, conditions cannot be imposed. Nobody has betrayed you or set a trap for you; it was you yourself who came here with your threatening troops, besieging the Lord's House and threatening the lives that gather here for a festival of love. You willingly came in here after having sent a group ahead of you to prepare the setting where your pride would prevail.

"I, too, experienced war firsthand when I was on the earth, and since my battle is against internal enemies and not external ones, I fell into the hands of those whom I believed were my adversaries. I was thrown into prison and endured the shame that prepared me for the Lord's call afterward so that I could love the brothers of that city where I was reduced to what I really am: nothing!

"It was there, however, that my Lord set me free and granted me the honor of serving Him.

"Don't you think the same might be true regarding you, my friend, that even though you do cultivate war, you are not really a combatant, but someone in need of light and understanding?"

After a brief silence in the dialogue, interrupted by the shouting outside and the clamor of those who were accompanying their defenseless and violent chief, he stated firmly:

"The gates of this Home of Jesus are wide open and its defenses will be lowered to allow you to leave and go back to your domain, where you can feed yourself on your own evil up to the moment when rebirth in the physical body carries you to the earthly stage, without support, without lucidity, in madness or dullness of mind, in paralysis or physical deformity... '

"Open the doors to the room," he instructed with the same gentle voice.

This unexpected attitude puzzled and disconcerted us.

The fluidic defense surrounding and guarding the institution was immediately lifted.

Outside, all kinds of infernal shouting, hooting and threats resounded in the air.

The attacker, in his ridiculous vestments displaying all the trappings of orthodoxy in his religious bigotry, glared at the Messenger of love, turned around, opened a passage through his group of minions, and started to walk out, ostensibly demonstrating victory.

However, before he reached the door, a cone of magnificent light came down from the Infinite and enveloped the wretch, who felt a jolt going through him while an incomparably beautiful voice asked him:

"Where are you going, my son?! What have you done to yourself?! There is only one way forward: the way of love."

At the same time, a lovely spirit condensed into human form. She advanced toward him from the outer side and stretched out her arms, asking:

"Eliachim, my son! How long have we been apart? I have come in search of you because there is no heaven for a mother whose son is suffering in the flames of unhappiness. Do not compromise your fate any longer. It's me, your mother Sara. I was martyred alongside you, but I forgave those who tried unsuccessfully to destroy us."

The impetuous rabbi stopped short, dumbfounded at the unusual spiritual event, and unable to resist the energy coming from his mother's spirit, he fell to his knees, howling in wild pain that tore at his insides.

"Oh, Mother! I'm just a miserable wretch forgotten by Adonai,"[35] he managed to say in unspeakable anguish. "No one loves me, and I have made hatred my liquor of choice. I get drunk on it more and more, waiting for annihilation."

"My dear son!"

The noble lady approached the wretch and wrapped him in indescribable tenderness, hugging him as she knelt by his side, as only mothers can do.

Brother Joy approached them with tears streaming down his face and completed the unforgettable scene, saying gently:

"Yes. You have just begun to live in true freedom. Take advantage of it! This is Jesus' answer to your pleas, showing how much He loves you...

At seeing the surrender of their chief, a significant number of those who accompanied him also pleaded for support and were assisted by the Templars, who, like all of us, had tears of joy and gratitude to heaven.

An unexpected melody of praise to Jesus was heard, sung by faraway spirit voices, while well-prepared workers from the institution assisted those who were surrendering to love.

Dr. Bezerra and the rest of our team watched the events, filled with deep emotion.

The victory of the good is always a life lesson.

---

[35] "After the exile (6th century BC), and especially from the 3rd century BC on, Jews ceased to use the name Yahweh for two reasons. As Judaism became a universal religion through its proselytizing in the Greco-Roman world, the more common noun *elohim*, meaning "god," tended to replace Yahweh to demonstrate the universal sovereignty of Israel's God over all others. At the same time, the divine name was increasingly regarded as too sacred to be uttered; it was thus replaced vocally in the synagogue ritual by the Hebrew word Adonai ("My Lord")." www.britannica.com. – I.R.

Soon, asleep in his mother's arms, Eliachim ben Saddoch was transferred to a special place on site, where mediumistic meetings took place.

The venerable lady thanked the *Angel of Assisi* and the rest of us, and before returning to her own sphere, she prayed:

"Lord of Israel and of all nations!

"May you always be praised for the greatness of your love, the mercy of your forgiveness, and your compassion toward your wayward children.

"Your greatness cannot be measured, nor can your laws of justice be fully understood.

"We submit always in complete trust to your designs, for they lead us to plenitude.

"Out of your mercy and compassion, receive the prodigal son back into your bosom.

"From all of us who love you, our perennial gratitude."

Her emotion was patent.

She entered the tube of light and dematerialized before our eyes dewy with tears.

Likewise, the *Saint of Assisi,* after brief words of affection and gratitude to Hermano and Dr. Bezerra, accompanied by his devoted brothers, returned to his own blissful sphere, leaving us filled with unsurpassed joy.

In a choked voice, Hermano approached us and bowed his head in gratitude and peace, uttering a prayer of reflection and joy beyond words.

We looked at the clock on the wall, which marked 3:30 a.m. of the day headed for the light.

CHAPTER 11

THE ENLIGHTENED ACTIVITIES CONTINUE

All of us were jubilant. We could not remember anything like it on our evolutionary journey. The chords of love sang tenderly within us as we experienced an unprecedented elation.

In a different state of mind, the Rabbi's followers outside were clamoring for his release, threatening to lay siege to the institution for as long as it took.

Assistance to his companions inside continued in an atmosphere of kindness. Some were taken away; others were released, fleeing the building to join those outside. Visibly touched by all that had happened, Anacleto approached Dr. Bezerra and thanked him for his extraordinary assistance.

I myself could not absorb all the fascinating events I was witnessing.

As soon as possible, I asked Dr. Bezerra about Saint Francis's decision to open the exit doors for the rebel.

He was not at all put off by my naive question, and kindly replied with a smile:

"Our Blessed One knew that the mother of the spiritually ill rabbi was on her way and that with her power of love and kindness she would get through to him during the difficult ordeal.

"Cultivating a destructive sentiment like hate for nearly five centuries condenses to such an extent in the core of the spirit that no words can dilute it. It takes the irrepressible power of unlimited love to alter this consolidated energy.

"At that moment, rather than explanations and discussions, something crucial was required that would shock him with surprise and enchantment in such a way that he would lose control over his reasoning and the infamous purposes he had cherished for so long.

"Wrapped in the vibration of universal love, the words of the *Imitator of Jesus* were aimed at creating an emotional arena for the happy reunion. None of us possesses the sublime power that he attained through selflessness and the perfect imitation of Jesus. Only those who are able to love indiscriminately can change the unfortunate course of someone who has surrendered to folly and dissipation. St. Francis knew that the rebel could not actually leave the building, since, from the moment he first entered the room he began to benefit from the surrounding psychosphere, thus gradually releasing the constrictive, unhealthy layers that asphyxiated him and to which he had adapted.

"After having been blessed by the light, the human being can never choose the darkness."

"What is going to happen to the rabbi now?" I asked.

"He will soon awaken in our colony," Dr. Bezerra answered joyfully. "He will be assisted at length by our psychotherapists, who will help him with his conflicts in preparation for what he will experience due to his tremendous rebellion and the turmoil and problems he caused his discarnate and incarnate brothers and sisters…

"As soon as possible, he will endeavor to free the hundreds of cohorts he deceived and forced to live in the infernal region where he was hiding out. He will contribute to changing the behavior of all of them, victims of their own and his insanity.

"None can run from their conscience forever. They will awaken at the proper time in order to start on a new pathway at the point where they went wrong.

"He will be shown that the persecution and infamous death he suffered are rooted in days long passed, when, together with Elijah, he put the worshipers of Baal to the sword with unparalleled cruelty and rage on the banks of the Kishon River.

"Many of the victims of the Inquisition bore the vestiges of that ancient massacre inscribed within their being because they had cruelly assailed worshipers of the pagan god, as if a moral wrong could be redressed through the criminal behavior of those who say they are responsible for the destiny of others.

"Nothing happens without being connected with previous events. Ultimately every victim is a recovering tormenter before the Divine Codes."

He paused, deep in thought.

Touched in their innermost fibers, Petitinga and Jésus, who had been following everything and had helped with removing the remaining spirits, conversed, truly sensitized.

Jésus asserted:

"I still bear the unspeakable wounds of having been a criminal executioner in the fourth and fifth centuries, when, in a mad lust for power while in the service of Rome, I razed towns, villages and entire cities with unusual savagery, culminating in the awful sacking of Rome itself in 410, a few years before I discarnated. Later, still fascinated by the lying glories of the world, I committed heinous crimes through intrigue at the French court. I murdered Huguenots at first, and then Catholic rebels and victims who still cry for help in La Rochelle...

"The leprosy that took me during my last incarnate journey was the perfect medicine for the long illness that my spirit bore and for which only time and work can serve as the final, liberating therapy. So, I can just imagine what is in store for that unfortunate brother as he begins another chapter in his life... I saw myself in him and I bow down before the sublime burden of purifying suffering, thanking its presence."

Agreeing entirely, Petitinga added:

"I have also known persecution and difficulty firsthand for having embraced Jesus' consoling doctrine unveiled by Spiritism. In those heroic days at the beginning of the first quarter of the twentieth century, the intolerance of the clergy on both sides of life was powerful and tenacious. In view of the sufferings starting in the early stages of my adherence to the grand faith, the vinegar of such suffering overflowing my anguished heart forced me to explore my inner world, and there I discovered the underlying causes of the illuminative process.

"Today I bless each and every trial, seeking in the works of charity the care and support I need for inner renewal, simultaneously sharing with my neighbor all that heaven has offered me in a rich harvest of peace and joy."

It was time to take the incarnate guests back to their homes, with the assistance of the workers of *love* and *charity*...

A large number of spirits who had entered the room with the rabbi and stayed there after his surrender decided to leave, fleeing in a stampede. They were allowed to leave because free will is always the first option, making room for processes of expiation in the future if rebelliousness is long-lasting.

As they arrived outside, they shared the news about their commander's surrender, generating panic and disorder among those who used to serve him... When some of the more audacious ones discovered that they were now free from his terrible control, they fled in search of their own destiny, whereas others returned to the caves whence they had come.

The event was inconceivable to them. They had attributed excessive power to the rabbi, and there would soon be a conflict to elect who would replace him in the regions that served as their dwellings. There are always fierce disputes among those who are evil. They attack each other due to the unhappiness that afflicts them, deluded by arrogance and their macabre exploits.

Thus, left to their freedom but never abandoned by Divine Providence, they would be taken care of by both time and the divine laws, guiding them to the good at the proper time.

Our task involved the insane rabbi and a number of his accomplices in need of assistance and mercy, which they now received.

Afterward, since there were a few who had lost control of their mental faculties, as a result of being demented and victims of zoanthropy, workers of the Gospel of Love and Charity took them to one of the institution's special rooms. There they would receive appropriate therapies to free them from their deforming hypnosis and indescribable afflictions.

With the area round about the Center nearly empty of the members of the hosts of evil, I observed the density of the unhealthy psychosphere and the countless thought-forms hovering where they had been a short time ago.

Their coarse psychical emanations and emotional exteriorizations had given way to a dark cloud still containing the exclamations of hatred, the groans and the aberrations that typified such hosts.

Under the guidance of Dr. Bezerra, specialists in ambient hygiene began using devices to cleanse not only the air but the ground, which had become contaminated with harmful idioplasmic fixations.

The work of preserving the environment is highly important for spiritual activities that have to operate within it.

In order for activities involving fluid and energy therapy conducted under special conditions to attain the desired success, they are subjected to many conditions and circumstances, including local hygiene. That is why precautions are taken so that mediumistic meetings involving healing, fraternal counseling and assistance take place in rooms reserved for such endeavors, in light of the defensive and sterilizing measures necessary to free them from the psychic miasmas of patients from both planes who flock there for help.

The day dawned radiant, and after all our work of cleansing and preserving the environment, we saw the sun in all its strength and majesty, blessing life on the planet.

Moreover, feeling much better that morning than on previous days, Anacleto met with the Center's president for an uplifting conversation, which I was allowed to listen in on.

The two met in a private parlor, where the formerly troubled Anacleto confessed to his friend and fellow worker in the Spiritist endeavor what had happened to him recently.

"I have had curious, strange dreams," he said, trying to recap his memories.

"I see myself right here with other members of our Center in very serious meetings of assistance for myself and others in need.

"Unfortunately, many of the details escape me. I can remember only incidents having to do with my own concerns and spirit-related obsessive disorders. You are aware of the fact that I have gone through a very bad period in my life since Margrete's discarnation. She was my mainstay, my moral security... Without her physical presence, my spiritual resistance faltered and I let myself indulge in behaviors incompatible with the Gospel of Jesus, culminating recently in wicked acts and outrageous conduct."

As he talked of his moral laxity, his emotions began to benefit him with honest repentance, leading him to the extreme truth:

"In the madness that gripped me, when I became the moral breech for evil to get in, I stole money from our Center, which I will refund at the first opportunity. I'm counting on your benevolence and compassion in my need for support and the opportunity to recover.

"I have come here to hand in my resignation to the board so that my illness will no longer impede the work for the good, which is characteristic of our institution."

"Sincerity is the seal that precedes any reparation; the courage to face one's error and resume healthy conduct."

The noble president took Anacleto's hand in a fraternal, lofty gesture and answered him with kindness:

"You, my brother, have never been worthier to continue your position than you are today. We all deceive ourselves and we have the right to start afresh, to find the best way to recover. I'm asking you to remain at our side, helping us and helping yourself. Our coworkers have been worried about your behavior. I will tell them about our meeting, but without going into the details. Everyone will give you the vote of confidence you deserve so that together we may follow the pathway of Jesus to the final moment...

"Meanwhile, continue to receive passes in order to increase your spiritual strength, and your work will do the rest for your full recovery."

Hermano was benevolently inspiring the confessor while at the same time helping him vent all his conflicts in a cathartic conversation that produced excellent results.

During the course of the meeting and the effect of the change in Anacleto's mental focus, the ovoid magnetized to his crown chakra became more agitated, emitting inarticulate sounds expressing anger and aggression. As the conversation proceeded down the path of peace and moral health, and Anacleto's thinking turned fully to the good, the suction-like tube that kept the ovoid connected loosened and unraveled, causing the ovoid to fall to the floor.

As if he had been waiting for that to happen, Dr. Bezerra picked it up with his own hands and spoke to it softly:

"Sleep now, my brother, and rest. You are weary and have suffered too much to continue this inglorious battle. These are new days of hope and you need inner harmony to choose the way forward as soon as you are free of this painful injunction.

"Never doubt the love of our Father; He never forsakes us.

"You are in this condition by your own free choice. Life's invitation to harmony and happiness is everywhere, but unfortunately, human beings frivolously choose the lubricous pleasure of just one moment to the detriment of lasting joy won by effort and sometimes sacrifice, which is very well-compensated.

"Devoted brothers will take you to a hospital where you can recover from your altered form, and a future reincarnation will complete your work of renewal and peace.

"May God keep you in blessings of harmony!"

The patient's agitation subsided and Dr. Bezerra handed it to two of the Center's diligent nurses standing by.

"Now, Anacleto will find it much easier to self-overcome. Since he has resolved to change his behavior, his attunement and his mental vibratory fields have become altered, thus releasing him from the avenger who had filled his mind with outrageous ideas in their lengthy hypnotic exchange.

"Spirit-related obsessions begin to loosen their constrictions on patients when the latter resolve to change the mental landscape that harbors spirit-parasites, sustaining them by means of their energetic tonus. That is why we did not free Anacleto from this last exploiter but favored him with freedom of psychotherapeutic choice derived from his own will."

I finally understood the benefactor's attitude when he had helped Anacleto during the aforementioned meeting, leaving that one sickly connection alone when, apparently, he could have broken it.

In fact, if he had broken it, what would be the patient's merit in receiving assistance without any conscious cooperation on his part, with no interest in changing his moral behavior?

The divine laws are very wise and those who know them profoundly can behave in the healthiest and most just way possible.

Jubilant at the outcome relating to our wayward brother, we spent the day in assistance activities at the institution.

That evening, at the usual time for studying *The Gospel according to Spiritism,* followed by passes and fraternal assistance, we rejoiced at finding the young Martina accompanied by Philippe and looking very well.

She was still immersed in thought, reading Jesus' message and letting herself become impregnated by its content.

Ever since our first meeting, when she had been induced to enter the institution, she had not returned to the brothel and had prevented any communication from her incarnate exploiter.

Now, she was listening to the message with tears born in the heart and streaming down her face. The lecture was about *discarnate enemies,* which touched her deeply since she was completely ignorant about such interaction, although she did know about it in a deformed sort of way from traditional religious lectures and common superstitions.

She realized that she was probably included among those who suffered their pain-filled domination and she promised to make radical inner changes.

Having benefited from the passes, she immediately sought further fraternal assistance to confirm that she was ready and willing to assume motherhood, in spite of the many risks, including being hounded by her exploiter, the brothel's owner and the natural difficulties she would face as a single mother...

In the process of her reincarnation, her mother was taken by unparalleled joy at hearing that her daughter was going to go through with the pregnancy.

Our mentor, who had accompanied the dialogue with us, whispered:

"The victory of the good is always the end result of any commitment. More lives are always redeemed by love.

"Let us continue our work of enlightening consciences and illuminating lives."

The night wore slowly on...

CHAPTER 12

THE STRUGGLES SUBSIDE

During the evening hours, various kinds of tormented people were arriving at the institution of love and charity. Some were depressed; some were in a lamentable state of obsession caused by malevolent spirits; others suffered from paranoid schizophrenia; still others were disturbed by torturous economic problems; but the vast majority were victims of existential problems...

The need for assistance compelled them to take part in Spiritist activities, given the expectation of achieving release and success as if by magic.

There are still mistaken ideas about Spiritism, the natural effect of widespread ignorance about the subject, as well as baseless information.

The Comforter promised by Jesus came to offer moral comfort to human beings, but also a sure guideline for them to acquire awareness regarding life's responsibilities, understanding that effects that result from negative actions cannot be stopped, but can be mitigated by ennobling actions. Moreover, Jesus explained that the *Paraclete* would repeat His words, which would be forgotten, and would also convey *new things that could not be understood during His lifetime.*

Thus Spiritism's mission is to illuminate the human conscience, teach individuals to find peace for themselves under the inspiration of the Most High, and reliably lead those who search for Him, providing them inner harmony and joyous living.

At that time the auditorium was being prepared for the weekly doctrinal lecture, after which collective passes would be given along with special passes requested beforehand by those most in need.

The evening's highly inspired speaker addressed a topic from *The Gospel according to Spiritism*, found in chapter V, entitled "Current and Prior Causes of Afflictions."

A matter of great current relevance, it was treated with logic and sentiment, leading the audience to think about the justice of reincarnation and the elements necessary for a life of balance and health.

After the lecture, which had been filled with vibrations of harmony and salutary spiritual fluids, those who had requested special interviews went into an adjoining room while everyone else remained in the area for the bioenergetic treatment.

We were assisting the pass-giving mediums, when our mentor was approached by an elderly discarnate woman. She had come there to request special help for her grandson, who at that moment was being assisted by an incarnate fraternal counselor.

Summoned mentally, we accompanied the other team members and followed a dialogue involving a depressed young man, who also suffered constrictive obsession by a callous and vengeful spirit. The discarnate's appearance was repulsive and enabled us to see that he was taking on a wolfish appearance... Coupled to the young man, perispirit to perispirit, the discarnate benefited from his energies, absorbing them through the *sacral* and *crown* chakras, while at the same time inducing him to escape through suicide...

The patient seemed dazed and could not coordinate his ideas in a balanced manner. He had difficulty thinking and conveyed that he was unhappy, that he did not know what to do with his life – according to what he told the attentive listener. He was undergoing psychiatric treatment and the drugs he was taking were very powerful; however, they could not reverse his depression, and seemed only to aggravate his condition. He was ready to stop the therapy, but he felt urges to jump out of his tenth-floor apartment window, seeking inevitable death.

"In the meantime," he explained with difficulty, "my grandmother appeared to me in a dream to help me.

"The next morning I felt a peace that I couldn't remember having felt before, but then the strange sensations returned and the impulse to leap into the void became acute...

"At home, I'm tormented by my father," he lamented with a trembling voice. "He thinks I'm crazy and lazy, which torments and frightens me even more. If it weren't for my mother's support, I would already have solved the problem..."

He paused and let himself be overwhelmed by the emotion of tears.

He was not yet 25 years of age, despite his physical deterioration, which made him look prematurely old.

Inspired by his spirit guide, who showed compassion for the patient, the counselor explained to him:

"Not every disease is just a disease. As you heard during the lecture a while ago, we come from previous existences, in which we did not always act with sober and dignified conduct. And due to our negligence, we harmed others who could not forgive us. Then death took both of us, and the consequences of our behavior remained written on our consciences. When we returned to the earth to give continuity to our evolution, we faced the liens that now accompanied us as redemption, suffering and disturbance caused specifically by those who suffered at our hands directly or because of us...

"Oftentimes these spirits, thirsting for revenge and desiring our failure, connect themselves to us mentally and send us their negative thoughts.

"Depression is one of the ways in which the Divine Conscience adjusts moral debtors, as guilt sleeping in our conscience resurfaces, generating conflicts and upsetting our neurocommunications. At the same time, however, those enemies furiously assail our weaknesses and aggravate our depression, poisoning us with their deleterious energies and their hateful thoughts. Over time, they assume almost complete domination over our will.

"A huge effort is necessary for us to untangle ourselves from the awful situation to regain our mental clarity and interest in life.

"You did very well in coming to us, and I believe it was your benevolent grandmother who inspired you to make this decision.

"Don't get discouraged, because you have just begun a new and happy phase in your life. By means of therapy through passes, the instructions you'll absorb during the public lectures, and your own mental effort, you'll be able to free yourself from your obsessor's tormenting constriction and the impulses that have been driving you to commit suicide... If suicide were able to resolve the problem it would be a way to break free from the persecuting spirit. However, because life goes on, those who escape their troubles through suicide will find that they have become much worse beyond the grave, adding to the pain imposed by their cowardly gesture.

"Resort to prayer and uplifting literature so that your thought abandons pessimism and starts to cultivate hope and existential joy, thus contributing to normalizing your neurocommunications, thanks also to the meds that will help you reestablish your balance.

"Go to the room for passes. You will benefit from the outset and will reprogram your life. You can only be helped if *healing* you want to help yourself. Doing your part is essential in this highly complex process."

Feeling much better, the young man stood up and returned to the room where he had been before.

A kindly medium approached and gave him passes with vibrations of health and peace.

On our part, our mentor also contributed with his own powerful energy, practically anesthetizing the callous, cynical discarnate obsessor who was mocking his victim...

Subsequently, Dr. Bezerra told the trusting grandmother that that very night her grandson would be assisted properly, beyond the help he had just received.

The young man, who had seemed almost defeated, was now renewed. Hopeful of being healed and accompanied by his grandmother, he left thinking differently about the problem that had been troubling him.

When true solidarity reigns among human beings and they all remember that the well-being of one results in joy for all, the pictures of suffering will change because mutual aid will predominate, overcoming selfishness and the primary passions responsible for the moral and spiritual disasters that plague the earth.

Spiritism's mission is to lead consciences to the irreproachable commitment to duty, with love as a secure and irreplaceable guideline. This does not imply accepting the absurdities of the insane, but having the courage to promote and live goodness in each and every situation, working for order and progress, both individual and collective.

Later, when the institution's usual duties were over, our benefactor invited us to join him and, at the consent of the benevolent Hermano, he scheduled the assistance to the depressed and obsessed young man.

In the early hours of the morning, all of us who had participated in rescuing the Jewish rabbi met to face the struggles that continue to intensify, especially in these serious days of planetary transition...

Dr. Bezerra appointed two of the Center's discarnate workers to fetch the young Raimundo – who was in partial disengagement during sleep – in order to continue his spiritual treatment.

The diligent friends returned a few minutes later with the sleeping spirit, to whom the conscious obsessor, railing in rage, was connected.

Since connections between victim and obsessor are always from perispirit to perispirit, as the spirit detaches from the body during sleep these connections remain intact, thus dragging the discarnate exploiter to the place where the spirit is or goes, whether lucid or asleep.

When Raimundo was awakened by Dr. Bezerra, the "friend to sufferers," he tried to figure out where he was. He recognized his grandmother, who had accompanied him from home, and he looked to her for comfort.

She immediately explained to him in a few words that this would be a highly significance moment for his life, urging him to remain calm and trusting.

Hermano began the meeting by offering a prayer anointed with love while Celestina concentrated deeply, amplifying the perispiritual faculties in a receptive attitude.

Dr. Bezerra applied dispersive passes to the patient and his enemy, freeing the persecutor, who then was immediately connected to the medium in trance.

He roared with anger:

"What's going on here? What's the meaning of this council or tribunal, which has forced me to come here against my will?"

With a gentle and kind voice, the mentor explained:

"This is neither a council nor a tribunal. It is a fraternal meeting aimed at an enlightening dialogue.

"As you well know, the exchange between the two spheres of life is continuous and meaningful. We are here in service to Jesus to free you from the suffering you have endured for decades because of your stubbornness.

"Nothing justifies your relentless persecution of young Raimundo, who is suffering your perverse injunction, threatening the destruction of his physical existence. All are reborn to progress, to right their wrongs and be released from the evil engraved on their delicate moral fibers…"

"Well, why the false concern for me? I'm the victim here. The sword of his wickedness reaped my life not too long ago. Why such benevolent concern for a wretch who ruthlessly claimed so many lives, including my own?

"We were brothers related by blood, but we had different ethical values. While I was a veritable Abel, he always showed himself to be an awful Cain… When our parents died, he was slated to take control of our assets and protect me because I was younger and inexperienced. But what did this wretch do instead? He took it all by illegal means, leaving me in poverty, the victim of terrible diseases and with no support or mercy. Madness took hold of me and I wound up on the street, completely abandoned, when my body gave out amongst other vagrants living under the viaducts of São Paulo...

"I watched my body rot away, devoured by maggots, and I suffered vampirization by other wretches who forced me into more horrors than those I harbored in my heart, because, still lucid, I swore revenge and drank all the acid of hatred and despair possible in order to recover what was mine...

"But how could I, if earthly justice belongs to the powerful, who can bribe anyone to get what they want?! I had pursued many legal avenues in vain. As if stealing my inheritance wasn't enough, informed of my desperate situation, he hired thugs to scare me and who nearly beat me to death. As a result, I caught a cruel disease that devoured me up to the last remnants of my lucidity...

"One day I finally freed myself from the vampires and regained my freedom. I found him in a new body marked by the conflicts of his infamy. I realized that I had suffered the hellish claws of evil for decades as I gathered the strength for revenge.

"Since I felt attracted to that traitor by some unknown force, I realized that I could be the judge in our battle, so I resolved to make his mental imbalance even worse in my eagerness to see him come back to this side, where I've been gleefully waiting to do to him what he did to me out of greed and treachery...

"There's no worse pain than being betrayed by an ambitious and coldhearted brother! Only by doing the same thing to him can his victim find peace-of-mind."

This explanation was made in a tone of suffering and retaliation with unusual inflection. His hatred was mingled with bitterness and the desire for revenge. Writhing in the mediumistic apparatus – Celina – the spirit was shrieking, producing a sticky drivel that the medium exteriorized with eyes inordinately open.

Dr. Bezerra let him express all his anguish and then spoke to him in a fatherly voice:

"Yes, we do understand your pain and you have all our sympathy. All of us have experienced very similar moments in the forge of reincarnations. The aggressive and malevolent instincts that dominate our spiritual nature promote these terribly unfortunate situations.

"Mythological tradition says that God placed a sign on Cain so that while he was alive he would expiate his crime against his brother Abel. The sovereign laws have also engraved on Raimundo the guilt that has accompanied him on his incarnate journey in order for him to recover, rendering unnecessary your cudgel of justice – which makes you a tormenter and no longer a victim.

"What attitude can we learn from Jesus on Calvary, after he was betrayed by Judas, denied by Peter, the brother-friends chosen by Him, and all the people who had received mercy and life through His hands? It was overall forgiveness for all those who struck Him, who failed to recognize Him, who crucified Him. This is because only forgiveness has the liniment to reduce the purulent rawness of the wounds of the heart and soul."

"But I don't have the strength to forgive him," the other retorted.

"Even though you can't forgive him now," explained the mentor, "give yourself the chance to experience the happiness of being released from the one you have clung to for so long. As long as hatred – the iron and fire of despair – thrives in your sentiments, it will be molded in the core of your being, like a wolf stalking the lost sheep. Devouring the sheep will not solve the problem, because your problem is internal; it is the seat of insanity that never ends, but should. Take a look at yourself, at the loss of your human form as a result of the wolf-like fixations you have harbored, like an animal anxious to consume its prey.

"You are a child of God, who loves and knows your suffering. However, He is the Father of both of you. He will correct the ingrate and invite the former victim to evolve. In the biblical myth, Abel was replaced by Seth, thanks to God's love. In the same way, let your tormenting memories die and be reborn in the form of the other brother who came afterward."

"But what about justice? Will he just go on living happily while I stay in the shadow of despair forever?"

"No, that will not happen at all," replied the wise mentor. "Marked by the memory of guilt, reincarnating under these circumstances due to his heinous crime, he has the conditions for suffering this purifying depression while the reproductive system you've been exploiting has presented serious, anguishing impediments since adolescence. In fact, it is one of the psychological causes of the disorder that you have been taking advantage of to complicate matters."

In the meantime, Petitinga and Jésus were applying healthy energies to the tormented obsessor to alter his degenerating appearance and lessen the impact of his resentment and desire for revenge.

Giving a signal to Raimundo's grandmother, she approached the rebellious spirit and said to him:

"Don't you recognize me, Melquiades? I was the mother of both of you during those stormy days... I returned to the real world before your father did, and since then I have sought solace for the loss of our dear son, like Eve in the Bible praying to God to give him back...

"That is how I found our unhappy Cain again. I also found the suffering Abel, who needs to become a complacent Seth for us all to be happy.

"Your father returned with him, and today in the physical world, he is making him pay for his excesses. He hates him and upsets him with taunts that come from his embittered unconscious. Don't you think making him pay double is too much? How long will it continue without both you and your father being held accountable? Then there will be only another change of position, where the one who is persecuted today, as the victim of those whom he wounded yesterday, will also clamor for justice. It becomes a wheel of endless suffering that needs to be broken by love."

The dazzled wretch listened to her, utterly surprised, his mouth agape, weeping copiously and unable to say anything.

Trembling and stammering, he looked toward the sweet, pleasant voice and said:

"You know all my pain... The despair is driving me mad... I hate with all my heart... This desperation has no end... I long to snatch him back here to the world of infernal darkness and torture him, without ever destroying him."

After a harrowing silence, he let out a cry of despair and begged:

"Have mercy on me. I'm suffering a madness that never stops consuming me. Make me forget, only forget, because I just can't stand this unbearable burden, this pressure that tortures me inside."

"Here I am, son of my heart. I'm still the mother who loves you very much and I, too, am suffering with your pain.

"Both of you are my children. Both of you are in need of love and opportunity. Sleep in the grace of the Father who never punishes us, who never wants misfortune for anyone, no matter who. Wait for a tomorrow that will dawn smiling on you – on all of us.

"Rest now, son of my heart, and as you sleep, reshape the dark landscapes of your mind. Afterward we will work together for the ingrate's redemption, and will help your father, who has also slid down the pathway of animosity of unknown cause to him."

She took him in her arms, as if he were the child of yesteryear and removed him from the fluids of the medium, who began to recover from the unhealthy discharges transmitted by the spirit patient.

After she handed her sleeping son over to the diligent nurses, the joyous woman thanked Dr. Bezerra, who was also touched in his sentiments of love, and then left.

Raimundo had been watching the entire incident without understanding it, when Dr. Bezerra took his hands and explained softly:

"Today a new dawn has broken on your life. No matter how long it has lasted, all suffering finally reaches the stopping point... That is because love is the law that reigns supreme throughout the universe. Start down the path again with love, looking to rehabilitate yourself from past burdens that follow you like a vile shadow.

"For some time yet, you will have to face the depressive disorder you rightly deserve. Take the time to ponder the size of your former excesses and consider the grand resources available to you for your self-enlightenment and your service to society.

"When you wake up, you will have but a faint notion about this contact with us, but everything that has happened will be stored in your unconscious such that the temptation of arrogance and crime will no longer find shelter in your sentiments.

"May the Lord of blessings bless you with His mercy and peace!"

Then he induced him to sleep and asked for him to be taken back home, which dedicated coworkers did immediately.

I knew that physical sleep is an excellent opportunity to experience the spirit world, the natural return to the *country* of origin. Each individual is drawn to the appropriate vibratory field out of affinity, either taking astral journeys to other levels and regions for learning, or to areas of darkness and pain, according to his or her compatible aspirations.

Moreover, I saw that the law reigning in the universe for thinking beings after the law of love is the law of tireless work, which is charged with promoting them up the evolutionary ladder.

Inactivity is the deception of the senses, for in a simple change of activity we recover and are motivated to continue.

COLLECTIVE ASSISTANCE

The following day we continued to take part in the usual activities at the Spiritist Center as we needed the right psychical conditions for the services that would take place during the late hours of the night.

We had been informed by Petitinga and Jésus that Dr. Bezerra planned to summon the spirits that had been collected by the Knights Templar in order to assist them according to the needs of a good number of them. Those who were suffering from zoanthropy would receive appropriate aid in the spirit community in the spirit world because it was better equipped. However those who were merely deranged, hypnotized by the rabbi and subjected to extremely painful demands due to their ignorance of the reality of life were in need of guidance in order to renew themselves and return to practicing the good for their own evolution.

The assistance work was increasing by the moment at the institution – that blessed workshop of love – because, by keeping its doors open to the suffering on both planes, it was constantly being visited by discarnates and incarnates in want and despair.

Thus both admission and assistance were carried out very carefully in order to keep the idle, the wicked and the fraudsters out. There never seemed to be enough time for the assistance, which was always offered calmly and harmoniously, with careful planning, without improvising, as is always the case with spiritual responsibilities under the sure direction of high-order mentors.

A true center of spiritual benefits, a large number of benefactors would come there to attend to loved ones still in the physical body, as well as those who had been misguided and had found themselves in regions of bitter suffering, or in need of personal learning and training. Messengers of the light also taught a number of courses to discarnate students who wanted to be useful, but who had no experience.

With curiosity I accompanied a group of discarnate attendants who were in charge of visiting those who requested help via correspondence or request by third parties...

Those attendants who aspired to a more conscientious service would start out under the supervision of specialized instructors, who would go to applicants' homes to surmise disturbing problems and work on beneficial measures in their behalf.

Aid, assistance and visits were frequently requested. Names and addresses were put in a special place in order to be noted by workers who, from that moment on, chose to assist the afflicted.

Visits were made either when the applicants were at home, or late at night as they slept, when they could receive the benefit of instruction, passes, or inspiration that would guide them in their daily lives.

At the appointed time, with the group of mediums present in meditation, Dr. Bezerra, the *Doctor to the Poor*, addressed us with kindness and wisdom:

"For quite some time now, the damage caused by continuous incursions by the rabbi's minions to persecute the

Spiritist hosts in Brazil and elsewhere – especially in the Land of the Cross[36] – has been incisive.

"The moment he grasped the fact that Spiritism is the fulfillment of Jesus' promise that he would return, manifested in the Paraclete, that vile opponent started to infiltrate Spiritist activities at the human level, generating unease, disputes, unhappy competition, internal struggles, and disturbances manifesting through immoral conduct, spreading slander and all its harm... Reputable Spiritist organizations began to be visited by militants of evil, along with others who delight in harassment and generating obstacles to progress, encouraging fights and noisy arguments, completely forgetting the well-disseminated but little-applied lessons of the Gospel.

"Messengers of the Light, concerned about the insurgency, manifested in many places where harmony and fraternity should reign, and have drawn the attention of improvident workers who believe that they themselves are undefiled. They affirm that error is always practiced by others; hence they cannot truly awaken to the endeavor of self-perfection and vigilance. These disrupters insidiously continue infiltrating the hosts of the good, threatening the unity of its work and diverting committed but fragile souls, who lapse into dismay and unbelief.

"Self-denial and selflessness, humility and sacrifice have fallen short, giving way to selfishness, pride and presumption – those generators of insane and destructive fighting, which repel those who seek peace and the good...

---

[36] Crux or the Southern Cross is a prominent constellation in the southern sky, easily recognizable for its cross-shaped asterism, the Southern Cross. It is always present in Brazilian skies. – I.R.

"Of course the deranged are not only connected with our brother rabbi. Many of them belong to different races and religions, because wickedness is not the heritage of one people or another, of one belief or another, but of the still primitive and proud human being per se...

"These enemies of the Light are taking advantage of the moral breeches in unvigilant workers, facilitating invasions by technicians in obsessions into places that used to be fortified by love, sowing discord, causing strife over mundane issues, inspiring divisions regarding doctrinal concepts, disturbing and destroying."

Visibly concerned, he continued in the same tone of voice, in which the vibration of seriousness and profound meaning stood out:

"The appeals of the mentors of various Spiritist Centers reached the Lord of the Harvest, who took measures through Brother Charity, inaugurating wherever His doctrine is presented a program for reestablishing ideals set on steadfast Kardecian foundations.

"Several of these measures have taken on a character of urgency, including those of our small group, which was responsible for putting a stop to the organizer of the aggressive ranks, and who is now undergoing restorative sleep, after which he will awaken under anguishing conditions for having practiced madness and folly for so long.

"Soon we will attend to those who have been brought to our Center. The same is happening at other serious Centers where mediumship is respected and practiced with honesty and selflessness, instructing enemies who have been brought there for dolorous but liberating communication.

"This is not an easy task, because nothing is as simple as it may seem at times. The goal is not only to ward off evil and evil discarnates, but to arouse workers to return to their original motivation – duty and charity – practicing what they preach to others.

"This is a very serious time in which workers should become aware of their responsibilities and prepare themselves so that they can help create the proper conditions for the happiness that will blanket the terrestrial planet someday. Those who are bound to Jesus have been given the irrefusable task of preparing for the advent of better days, without boasting and rashness, and without complicating the potential for its fulfillment.

"The good will ultimately achieve its intended goal, but all those who impede it consciously or unconsciously will be banished and will suffer the consequences of their insubordination, because today nearly all of us are aware of what is happening, as well as what will happen afterward...

"Our work in the spirit realm will be supplemented by conscientious Spiritists and, of course, by all citizens who fulfill their duty and carry out their commitments honorably.

"The faith that enlightens will facilitate implementing the program, but praiseworthy sentiments are what will characterize everyone entrusted with making the projects under development a reality.

"So, spreading the lesson of true fraternity – and living accordingly – enlightening the masses by example, awakening sleeping consciences with the clarions of beneficent endeavors, and overcoming the appeals of one's primitive passions in favor of self-realization – all these are the commitments of anyone invited to the land of hope."

Everyone was listening with mind and ennobled sentiment. He paused again and then continued:

"Since we have been honored by the opportunity to serve, let us spread the kingdom of God everywhere, singing hosannas to the Lord who loves us and goes before us.

"Now, let us pray and let heavenly inspiration touch us."

Diaphanous lights danced in the ambient.

Small groups of tormented spirits were led in one by one by the Templars, who showed joy at serving others as they had in the past, in the regrettable days of the Crusades. The groups were placed in the room, which had been enlarged beyond its physical space...

Exuding unhealthy emissions resulting from their emotional and spiritual state, the ambient psychosphere slowly began to change until the whole place was completely full.

The spirits in a state of perispiritual deformity – those who also had remained there the day the rabbi surrendered – were kept in a spiritual assistance area that communicated directly with our colony.

Nearly all of them were very uncomfortable and restless, some lethargic, others anxious and still others with an empty stare, clueless as to what was happening. These spirits, slated to become parasites coupled to the perispirit of unvigilant workers, were being held here for the benefit of all.

There was also a large number of troublemakers and mockers who seemed to want to continue the disturbance, but now had no means to do so.

Points of light passed through the unwholesome vibration-charged cloud and reached the tormented spirits.

After Hermano offered an emotional prayer rich with love, a young discarnate woman of about 20 years of age, dressed in a long white robe of delicate flowing tulle, began singing the 18th century Christmas carol *Adeste Fidelis* by John Francis Wade, which took us to a state of near-ecstasy.

O come all ye faithful: the lyrics of the sublime hymn roused us to remain in an attitude of vigilance for the service of the good in homage to Jesus.

As the hymn of praise spread throughout the room, harmonious vibrations modified the heavy psychosphere, providing dulcifying energies to everyone who breathed them and diluting the perverse ideoplasties.

When the music ended, our benefactor stood up and began speaking from the table where the mediumistic session was taking place. With us were a number of the institution's mentors and some incarnates in partial disengagement during physiological sleep:

"The peace of the Lord be with us!

"No matter how terrible the stormy night may be, the sunshiny day quietly arrives for renewal from any disasters that may have occurred.

"All afflictions – even the ones resulting from the sufferers' own stubbornness – find an alternative in hope and tranquility. So, no harm can remain too long. After fulfilling the purpose for which it was meant, affliction gives way to renewal, balance, and the hope for less-disturbing new commitments... *Healing*

"Deluded in our spiritual inferiority, many of us have walked along the edge of duty, only to tumble into the madness of self-gratification and the desire for domination. Some as victims, others as tormenters, we make up the vast legion of the children of Calvary, to which Jesus referred when he stated that it was for them that He had come.

"So, the time has come for us to meet Him, changing the mental and emotional behavior that we have indulged in during times of madness and wickedness, of willful stubbornness in error and negligence.

"The trumpet of spiritual renewal is sounding, announcing new times that are no longer in harmony with crime or the supposed superiority of some over others. We

143

are all born free, and are dependent on our actions. When they are good we experience joy, but when they are bad they enslave us.

"Till now you have chosen the shadowy pathway of crime and folly. You have adopted the conduct of rebelliousness, as if you were proud new Lucifers daring to confront the Divine laws. As a result of this aberration, you have fallen into the webs of the hellish suffering you have sown in many places, and which you have now begun to reap as bruising thorns. Do not rebel against the need to repair in tears the ill-fated experiences you went through with smiles, while others wept...

"The Lord does not want you to remain in the swamps of ignorance, and that is why he is giving you the liberating chance that has come to you in hymns of hope. Free yourselves from the bondage of your aggressive and base instincts, and increase the sentiments of love and compassion in your lives.

"Since the past cannot be undone, the consequences of your actions lie ahead of you, waiting for a solution that you will have to willingly adopt in order to enjoy the peace that you do not yet know.

"In your afflictions you will ask how such renewal, the work of rebuilding your lives, is possible.

"To those who are linked to Judaism, I will reply that in your holy books such as the Sefer ha-Bahir or Book of Enlightenment, and the Zohar or Book of Hope, the transmigration of souls through physical bodies is known as Gilgul Neshamot, and the Hasidim and the Kabbalists know that reincarnation is the sole means for human beings to regenerate themselves and repair the wrongs they have practiced for ages. Others, members of Christianity, are aware of the dialogue between Jesus and the scholar Nicodemus, where Jesus told Nicodemus, 'You must be born again to enter the kingdom of heaven... born of water (body) and spirit (a new personality)'...

"Reincarnation is the blessed school that fosters the development of the spirit's intellectual and moral values in its growth in pursuit of the perfection for which it is destined."

The disciple of Jesus paused in order to facilitate the understanding of his words.

As he spoke, the vibration of his voice and the content of his message created harmony in the ambient, calming the wretched spirits, inasmuch as was possible, enabling them to absorb the words, which reached their core and would remain imprinted there, even if they did not understand them at the time.

Dr. Bezerra continued:

"You obeyed the call of disorder and destruction because you were taking part in madness caused by the ignorance of God's Laws... Hypnotized by terror and punished by the Furies, you did what you were ordered to do without taking into account how grave it was. Now you have awakened to a new reality which imposes responsibility on you for your unpostponable acts and commitments.

"Your former chief, more unfortunate than all of you, is now asleep in order for his ill-fated memories to diminish so that he can start from where he stopped, dominated by raging anger and scorching hatred... He and the many others who submitted to him will advance along the same roads fraught with misfortunes that will call them to reparation. None are immune to the divine plan, doing what pleases them, without having to experience the effects of their acts, whatever they may be.

"However, the love of the Master Jesus for all His creatures exceeds anything we can imagine within our selfish limits.

"Your renewal starts today. Calm the anxieties of your heart and the torments of your mind so that you may grow inwardly and reach the sublime level of peace.

"May the Lord bless and enlighten all of us."

When he finished, the darkness that had hung in the air had almost completely dissipated.

Automatically, the Templar Knights began their assistance activities, distributing calming energies over the heads of sufferers, some of whom had been overcome by the tears of righteous repentance. Others came out of their stupor, and still others expressed surprise and wonder.

The hands of charity glowed with light derived from the sentiments of the kindly Templar pass-givers, who, since the terrible days of medieval darkness, had learned the art and science of serving their neighbor...

The rest of us also stood up and extended our hands toward the silent crowd, benefitting them with energies that entered them for specific purposes.

Dr. Bezerra's voice once again made itself heard while musical chords could be heard throughout:

"Sublime dispenser of blessings,

"When dawn breaks through the darkness of ignorance to announce the day of jubilation, those of us who serve You salute You as the Sun of Utmost Grandeur, and we pray that Your light may disperse all our wickedness, making way for the installation of the kingdom of love in our lives.

"We are Your erring disciples, who have returned to Your fold because of Your mercy, after having abandoned it along the evolutionary pathway.

"Receive us as we are so that we may learn to be as You want us to be.

"Our offer to Your magnanimous heart is no longer the cup of the gall of ingratitude or abandonment, but the commitment to be faithful to You in every circumstance we will face tomorrow, understanding that even suffering is a heavenly gift for our purification.

"Just as You received the repentant Peter and entrusted him with guiding the terrified disciples, and just as you sought out Judas in the infernal regions and granted him the opportunity of purifying rebirths, grant us also – all Your thankless disciples – the mercy of Your forgiveness in the form of inner renewal through countless mitigating reincarnations.

"Allow Your selfless messengers to remain with us in Your name, helping us in the process of enlightenment, such that all the darkness we have left along the pathway may become light, and enable us to resolve to move forward, whatever the price of redemption may be.

"Lord Jesus!

"Grant us Your sweet peace so that we may be worthy of You today, tomorrow, and always."

Sidereal harmonies hung in the room bathed in a light similar to moonlight.

The Templars and members of the Center were carefully leading the assisted groups inside the building for immediate transfer to the spirit colony, where they would be prepared for future reincarnations.

We finally understood the grandeur and power of love in the name of the Supreme Good, and also the dangers that surrounded communities dedicated to the blameless Crucified One.

The meeting ended. All the incarnate members were taken back to their homes and the rest of us sought the repose that would provide us with a better grasp of the sovereign codes of higher justice.

PRICELESS, INDISPENSABLE LESSONS

The following day during a break in the activities at the Spiritist Center that continued to serve as the base for our own activities, Dr. Bezerra called a meeting in the mediumistic room, which had been reserved for that purpose.

We met joyously, joined by the benevolent Hermano and a number of his aides, to listen to the wise words of our director.

After Dr. Bezerra offered a heartfelt prayer, he greeted us courteously and explained:

"In preparing for our excursion to attend to the urgent needs of the Spiritist movement – especially at this Center – we have avoided detailing the particular situations so that you would be less concerned. Nonetheless, ever since the first moments of our endeavor, we have known that the yeast of evil had spread to various other Spiritist Centers in Brazil, as well as in other countries that have received the blessings of the Comforter.

"Of course other groups are also receiving competent assistance, according to the superior plan that has called us to the special task entrusted to us under the auspices of Heaven.

"But in spite of that fact, we know that there have been dangerous infiltrations by Rabbi Saddoch's acolytes into various Centers, which are still under the injunction of evil interference...

"Concurrently, considering the moral and physical transition taking place on the planet, frenzied hordes of spirits that banded together in infernal caves are now assailing the activists of the New Era and are trying to spread the deadly pestilences of doubt, schism and destructive intrigues. And they are having a severe, damaging effect, as I have already mentioned...

"We cannot ignore the moral, spiritual situation reflected in today's politics and in the economy prevalent in the world, which is going through a very critical moment as powerful civilizations are collapsing under the blows of the law of progress, while others seem to be emerging to replace them, even if, for some, slave labor and disrespect for citizenship and people's freedom are the predominant agenda. Because of the interests that run nations in general, other nations try to ignore the heinousness of these authoritarian regimes so as to reap profits and form partnerships with their powerful economies, born in cruelty to people who suffer from their destructive demands."

The friend to the poor paused to gather his ideas, and then continued:

"In the days of the recent past, Islam began to be seen as the fastest growing religious doctrine on the planet. Instead of encountering the disgust of civilization, examples of terrorism and impiety by some of its members received support from insane incarnate minds and psychopaths who were not able to make a name for themselves otherwise, taking refuge in the dens of hatred and participating in their nefarious criminal

Islam, migrants

plans aimed at the death and destruction of the Western and Eastern cultures as well as in their respective nations, provided these plans were against the interests of other ethnic groups or factions of the same religious doctrine... With a few exceptions, its ayatollahs have not inveighed against this bleak situation – which is not supported by the Koran, their holy book – but have actually encouraged disorder, aiming to dominate the world with their proposals for violence on the one hand and submission to their morbid whims on the other.

"Accurate statistics, based on the laws of genetics, have established that, for the culture and civilization of an era to survive over time, basic levels of human reproduction are required to assist with economic and social development; however, this is not happening in Europe and North America... This risk of the breakdown of civilization has been offset by a massive Muslim immigration, which, with each decade, is reaching amazing population levels in host countries. It is also natural that the number of Islam's followers will increase and that fanaticism will grow, because these immigrants are rarely idealistic and cultured, but economically needy laborers. They hang on to the roots of their origin, and do not assimilate the knowledge or the language of the nations in which they have settled, preserving their habits and keeping their offspring limited by the walls of enslaving ignorance. It would seem inevitable that within a few dozen years these nations might become Muslim, which would not be regrettable, except that rejecting Jesus would be a danger to human freedoms and a big setback in the planet's evolution, thus hindering its renewal to a world of regeneration.

"Since no one, no force, can stand as an impediment to the divine plan, free spirits have been reincarnating in those countries and employing resources of virtual communication that facilitate contact with the West and the rest of the world, even under the dagger of the harsh laws that threaten those who contravene them... Consequently, these networks of social communication via the Internet have become an instrument for relationships and for warnings against the ills that those lands are undergoing at the hands of insane dictators, giving rise to the rebellion against suffering and the emergence of the so-called Arab Spring. A number of thrones have fallen and those who used to sit on them became victims of the same cruelty they used against their real or imagined enemies, losing their heinous lives in the same way. Dangerous, powerful men fled and hid in holes dug in the earth to hide their cowardice, only to be found like persecuted animals and then harshly imprisoned or killed with the same fury that these revolutionaries had been victims of... And the Spring continues, changing the geopolitics, in which the West has gotten involved in its eagerness to profit from the mineral wealth of those dead, desert soils...

"The serious problem that has not yet been considered involves the revolutionaries who topple tyrants by using the very same methods that they condemned these offenders for because of their crimes against humanity. Moreover, if they were to develop a taste and lust for power, which should pass through their hands, and begin to coerce those who yearn for freedom, gradually taking it from them, they would remain in control and postpone forever the fulfillment of the promises they made before the struggle...

"At the same time, these countries are composed of various ethnic groups that often have a culture and religious formation that differs from the primitive foundations of the Koran, giving way to various interpretations. This has created factions that hate each other, raising the risk of new internecine battles with incalculable damage to ideals, which for a time, fluttered on banners hoisted in fierce combats.

"Unfortunately, this behavior is happening in some of the nations that would have been transformed otherwise, and the new conquerors' promises have not yet been fulfilled...

"All these murderers of humanity were, and some still are, protected by the dominant religion, just as occurred in the West in the past, when religion determined who should rule, live, own property, die, go into exile, or be thrown into prison, before the French Revolution confronted the ruthless tradition and put an end to it. The same is now occurring in the region hit by the wave of the search for freedom and justice... As a result, there is eagerness for separation between the state and religion, reducing or making the unhappy and supreme power of the ayatollahs or clergy hungry for revenge disappear.

"Consequently, the possibility for the expansion of the Muslim faith to dominate Europe and a New America in the near future is retreating, if not disappearing, while the gentleness, compassion, mercy, love and charity of the divine Messiah will spread under other conditions to these exhausted nations, where His doctrine foundered – the victim of unscrupulous, ambitious priests and pastors...

"Most of humankind's wars have in some way or other always been caused by religion, which has rendered it loathsome. It is Spiritism's mission to change this concept through its fundamentals based on the certainty of immortality and Divine Justice through reincarnation, making all aware of the fact that one always receives to the extent that one has given."

Dr. Bezerra paused once more to give us time to mentally absorb his thought before continuing:

"For a few years now, promoters of new times have been reincarnating in those countries dominated by intolerance and hatred toward other nations, as well as in the latter, so that the curtains concealing the truth may open for it to be known without restriction. At the same time, spirit communications are breaking down the barriers erected by fanaticism regarding the text of the espoused religion, allowing for a broader understanding of life beyond the grave, setting aside the fantasies of a Dantesque Inferno and a Paradise enriched with sensual, erotic pleasures that intoxicate the physical senses, a view that will no longer prevail...

"Poets, thinkers, artists from various fields of beauty, scientists from the past and present – all will be returning to awaken the mind, assisting it with the evolution of fraternity amongst all peoples – one sole family composed of different races, blood and passions – in which all will enjoy the blessings of harmony.

"Similarly, truth's cantors from bygone days are reincarnating in order to assist with the great impulse of liberating progress.

"Jews, Muslims, Buddhists, Hindus, esotericists, adherents of other religious denominations, spiritualists or non-spiritualists in general, thinkers and scientists who are encouraged to consult the Bible or the sacred books that underpin their beliefs – they will all realize that reincarnation is the cleansing crucible for human impurities and the facilitator of the spirit's unending progress.

"We read in Exodus 20:5-6, recorded by Moses: 'Do not bow down to them and do not serve them, for I, Yahweh, your God, am a jealous God, visiting the sins of the fathers upon the children in the third and fourth generation of those who hate me, but acting with kindness or mercy to thousands of generations (rebirths) that love me and keep my commandments.'

"Again and again, we find in the Old and New Testaments the presence of reincarnations demonstrating the love and wisdom of God in regard to the progress of the spirit and its eagerness for perfection. The doctrine that holds that there is but one sole existence cannot explain all the apparent paradoxes existing on the earth regarding the human being, the differences and the events that mark them, the behaviors and the conditions of humanity, as well as the various races and peoples...

"Note that the Lord refers to Moses concerning His severity in the third and fourth generations, when the criminal spirit may already be reincarnated as its own grandson or great-grandson, which does not occur in the second generation, because in that one, of course, a different spirit is its son or daughter.

"Thus it is through reincarnation that the spirit purifies itself, until it releases its inner divine essence, ridding itself of every impurity deriving from the evolutionary process pertaining to the first levels of its development.

"Since it is unable to administer the love that solves all of life's problems, it experiences suffering, which removes its malevolent edges, preparing it for great achievements on the pathway to plenitude.

"So, with all that in mind, we are being invited to help our unfortunate brothers and sisters, who are set on preventing or creating obstacles to the glorious transition, generating difficulties for spiritual guests from another dimension to be reborn.

"Later, after we have visited a number of the Spiritist Centers that are suffering such obstacles, victims of invasion by pernicious spirits, with whom we will try to communicate, we will also converse a little with some of the immigrants from Alcyone,[37] who are in our beloved earth's psychosphere, adapting to its fluids and conditions, considering the fact that they have come here from already happy regions that no longer experience the suffering or constrictions of our planet.[38]

"Gazing at the future through the imagination illumined by the Beatitudes proposed by the Nazarene Prophet, we behold our world without dark shadows as it follows the plan of the gradual evolution of the light overcoming every kind of darkness, without the bitterness of suffering or the insanity of violence, because love, justice and freedom in hymns of blessedness and peace will reign.

"May the Lord be praised and served in His desires amongst us!"

When he finished, we were all truly amazed as we pondered the concepts presented. I, myself, had never even thought about the expansion of the Muslim doctrine, the ability of immigrants to conquer the world through the proliferation of their race and human reproduction, considering my expectations regarding the growth of the Christian doctrine completely renewed and capable of assisting the suffering wayfarers on the earthly vessel.

Fact is, nothing related to the progress of the individual and humanity is the result of chance. It is always the result of a well-designed plan for such purpose.

We spent the hours that followed in invaluable conversation, especially discussing Spiritism's historic mission in the troubled world of today.

---

[37] A third-magnitude star in the constellation Taurus: brightest star in the Pleiades. – I.R.

[38] See *Planetary Transition* by the same Spirit Author (LEAL Publisher, 2016). – I.R.

Might Spiritism be the religion of the future? I wondered, recalling the same question posed by Kardec. However, I realized that, due to the evolutionary differences of the planet's human inhabitants, this would not be the case; rather, Spiritism would be the *future of religions,* which would accept some of its paradigms rejected by them nowadays in order to sustain their theology, so far unable to explain all kinds of questions in the fields of science, philosophy and morality.

.

CHAPTER 15

AN OPPORTUNE INTERVENTION

That same night, workers from both planes met just as we had in previous days. We were waiting for workers from other Spiritist Centers, hit by the fury of Rabbi Saddoch's minions, to bring some of the most prominent combatants to our mediumistic meeting.

Within minutes, five spiteful, coarse, half-awake spirits were brought in, along with a group of others who bore lascivious expressions, fighting against the vibrational bands that enveloped them and led them to our room.

After Hermano opened the meeting, the mediums Celestina and Marcos went into a deep trance, attracting for fraternal dialogue two of the guests, who woke up connected to the mediums' expanding perispirits, simultaneously initiating a tortured and aggressive psychophony. Marcelo and Dr. Bezerra took action immediately, the latter choosing Rabbi Melchizedek, who was communicating through the transfigured Celestina.

We perceived the entire room filling with powerful fluidic defenses that held the other strange visitors within its range so that they could hear and follow all the details of the communications of their defiant leaders.

The rabbi raved like his chief before him:

"Only through treason could the cowardly disciples of the Lamb have reached us, intentionally ignoring the fact that we too have rights before the laws in force in the universe."

"Of course," Dr. Bezerra countered, "the same rights given to those who have fallen into your evil traps... Rights you have given yourselves to hurt, torment and erect obstacles to the work of the good, and to bring misfortune to others...

"You, my brother, call us traitors, we who use the resources of prayer and mercy instead of your mechanisms of harm, cruelty and hatred, with which you poison the unwary and drag them down into your heinous prisons, in pungent processes of obsession."

"We have the right to obey the authorities of our religion," reacted the exasperated communicator. "If it were not our obligation to obey their orders we would not have begun such a long and terrifying battle."

"You are right in saying you serve a wretched spirit, but one who has just surrendered to the truth in submission to the meekness of Jesus."

"Oh, there was no surrender. It was an arbitrary imposition due to the detestable method used to hold him in your vile trap.

"But you are wrong, my friend. Rabbi Saddoch willingly came here and entered our stronghold guided by his instinct for destruction. He was a victim of his own arrogance... He should have known that this Place is guided by and follows a plan prepared by the Lord of Life, that his attempt at invasion would prove fruitless, and that he was running the risk of falling into the web of his own impudence. Even so, he was encouraged by the success that a few of his followers were having here and at other Centers of love, so he did not stop at the impetus of carrying out his inferior purposes once and for all under the fierceness of his own violence."

"Well, what do you want from us, after all? We have nothing to do with this Center."

"Of course you have nothing against our Center; but in your rage you want to challenge Jesus' servants, setting traps for them, attacking them, and seducing them with your siren songs to drag them mercilessly under your domination."

"It's just that the promise of the crucified one who claimed to be our Messiah is false and heinous, and down through history, he has fueled bloody persecutions against Adonai's elect. But he was a false prophet who was judged according to what he deserved... So, it is only natural that we have always risen up against him through his wretched heirs and disseminators of the big lie. We will not rest until we have changed the structures of the true doctrine recorded in the Torah and the other holy books of our people."

"Listening to you expose your idea by using your sophist argumentation, one might think that you are right. Jesus is God's Messiah, not only for Israel, but for all humankind. No one has ever lived the truth as fully as He did – not even any prophet who came before or after Him, for all those who came to proclaim Him were short of His greatness. It was He who rose to meet the lower classes despised by the other social classes' deceitful prejudices cultivated by tradition and preserved in the synagogues... His ability to love and forgive has never been matched by anyone.

"The persecutions you mentioned were not by Jesus but by exploiters who took His teachings and turned them into temporal strength and power much different than His, which

He made very clear regarding commitments to God and commitments to Mammon. Giving in to the world's tempting allures, such exploiters abandoned Him and despised Him.

"We cannot judge and condemn the Jewish people for a crime that was perpetrated by the Sanhedrin and the Roman rulers, just as we cannot accuse all individuals of insanity because of their cruelty in the ancient wars against the Philistines and other vanquished peoples, or their slaughter of the worshipers of Baal and other gods. A religion that does not promote mercy or compassion, a people that does not respect the rights of other peoples – neither of these merit consideration. Their actions are appalling, but a chance must be given to their descendants, who are not responsible for the heinousness of their ancestors. Similarly, one cannot blame the Master of compassion for crimes committed by those who have betrayed Him over time, inflicting persecution and harm on all who displeased them."

Simultaneously, Marcelo was enlightening the second avenger with similar words, while the rest of us followed the dialogues, especially the one between Dr. Bezerra and Rabbi Melchizedek.

"You, my brother, can see that, on the pathways of Spiritism, the new disciples of Jesus are striving to reestablish the purity and loftiness of the principles He proposed in love, charity, and caring for one's neighbor, especially concerning those who are misfortunate or experiencing torments of any kind."

"Oh, all that is just part of the big scam," the Rabbi snapped, still in a rage.

It seemed that feeling touched by the benefactor's fluent truths, and showered by vibrations of kindness and compassion, he had decided to remain aggressive because he had absolutely no argument to justify his contemptible behavior.

"We have no interest other than your well-being and all those under the constriction of hatred and bitterness."

"You're the one who believes that; but we are happy about our purposes and accomplishments."

"In addition to being unfaithful to the truth, you, my brother, are insolent and presumptuous, because no one can be happy while persecuting and exploiting others and striving to cause their misfortune.

"We must warn you that all the evil you do will revert back to you. Let us consult Genesis 15, verses 15 and 16. It says: 'As for you, you will go to your fathers in peace and be buried at a happy old age. It is in the fourth generation that they will return here, because until then, the sin (meaning the crime committed) of the Amorites will not have been paid.'

"That means that as long as one's sin has not been redeemed, one cannot return to Adonai.

"Look: when you discarnated, when your flesh died and your physical life ceased in the tomb, where did you go? What heaven welcomed you, in spite of your having regarded yourself as the good shepherd that you should have been for your people? Instead, inclement hatred devoured you and left you with not one trace of spiritual knowledge. It pushed you into the abyss where you find yourself today, even after several centuries have passed. What kind of doctrine is that? It cannot even help its faithful at the most critical time of their existence as immortal beings.

"Use this moment to reflect and reconsider your bloodthirsty attitude and unhappy purposes against Jesus and His humble followers eager for love and mercy. According to that text from Genesis, reincarnation is imposed on all of us and none can escape it. It is a universal law. The Lord of worlds can call us to return to the body at any moment. How will you be reborn, my friend and brother? How are you going to escape the divine Law?

"Now is your chance – yours and all those involved in this winless war of evil against good, of violence against peace, of hate against love. How long are you going to prolong the great night that surrounds you?"

The benefactor was addressing all the guests that had been brought in for this climactic occasion.

Suddenly we heard weeping and exclamations, disavowals, pleadings for help that were attended to by the Templars and the Gospel workers from the various Centers, receiving them with kindness and mitigating their suffering during their painful awakening...

Dr. Bezerra touched the medium's forehead with infinite kindness and concluded:

"Only through the courage to review one's own situation can one find oneself first and then God.

"You, my brother, are not being judged or criticized. We are inviting you to a change of attitude, to an encounter with the happiness that awaits us all."

The mentor's hand, touching the patient's crown chakra through the medium in trance, became gloriously illuminated. The rays penetrated the rabbi's perispirit, causing him to erupt in a cascade of tears and mourning, like an unprotected child:

"Help me, O Lord God of Israel!"

He stood in tears mumbling Psalm 106, repeating verse 1: Praise the Lord: "Praise the Lord, for He is good; for his mercy endures forever."

And in self-affliction, he added:

"But I am unhappy and wretched, for I have not obeyed the Lord's commands. Woe is me!"

Our instructor said to him, compassionately:

"The Lord is gracious and merciful: 'Blessed are they who observe righteousness, who do justice at all times,' as the third verse of that chapter emphasizes. The righteousness and justice that must be practiced entails working on behalf of and showing mercy to all people – which you have not done. But do not torment yourself; continue to praise the Lord until the time of your personal victory."

There was a long silence, broken only by noisy weeping accompanied by exclamations, also joined in by the spirit communicating through Marcos as well as the other sufferers, who began to receive appropriate care from the teams of Jesus' workers.

Muted with emotion, Rabbi Melchizedek, with effort and embarrassment, managed to end the meeting, muttering:

"May the Lord make you to lie down in green pastures... And forgive me!... for His name's sake!"

He was of course referring to Psalm 23. He was welcomed tenderly by Petitinga and Jésus, who put him to sleep so that when he woke up, he would be at peace and would trust in God's sublime mercy.

We are all travelers on long journeys that are disrupted by foolishness and then resumed with *weakened knees*; all are in need of forgiveness and new experiences to repair and build the good within, in their sentiments and thoughts.

After these spirits were brought in to communicate and receive assistance, the room was prepared for the continuation of the scheduled activities.

A soft violet light slowly filled the entire room, which had become like a small Greek amphitheater open to the star-dusted sky and surrounded with rose gardens, myrtles and angelicas in blossom. A breeze brought in their fragrance, filling us with great joy.

It no longer looked like a normal room. It reminded me of some of the buildings in our sphere, where large gatherings and spectacles of beauty take place, leading our thoughts to Jesus.

The watchtower was also still in place, manned by members of the religious order of the past.

In the center, at the bottom of the circular staircase, there was a rectangular table, and next to it was a podium decorated with laurel leaves, symbolizing the victory of good over all evil.

The noble Hermano and Dr. Bezerra descended to the center, accompanied by us and workers from the Spiritist Center. Over a thousand spirits filled the galleries. Many of these were incarnates in partial disengagement during physiological sleep, obviously brought there by their spirit-guides.

In the meantime, the sound of masterfully played lutes filled the room and the same young woman as before sang a special solo exalting the grandeur of Jesus.

When she finished, with the audience emotionally enrapt, Dr. Bezerra prayed for divine protection for the work to be done that morning. When he finished, dozens of tall in stature, high-order spirits descended the stairs and glided toward the arena, encircling it and radiating a fascinating magnificent light.

Suddenly a tube of light was projected from On High, and within it condensed the *Saint of Assisi,* accompanied by a few of his closest disciples, calling to mind the glorious days of the past...

We could not hold back the tears of joy that flooded our eyes and streamed down our faces.

It was a sublime, unforgettable moment, in which all less-beautiful memories or those marked by any kind of suffering were forgotten.

With an expression illuminated by his profound inner peace, St. Francis approached the podium, which received a jet of light, much like what occurs in theaters to highlight certain scenes or persons. St. Francis was glorified with blessedness, in an attitude of unparalleled humility, stating:

"Brothers and sisters from the ends of the earth, and great souls from Alcyone:

"May the impeccable peace of the Lord Jesus be with us all!

"We are experiencing the great moment of a battle without quarter. It is a battle in which the armies of the Lord and Master will be armed with the instruments of love and mercy to restore the kingdom of meekness and love for everything and everyone on earth.

"Preserving the good in the secret chamber of people's hearts has been a major existential challenge, especially with the appearance of the first rays of light signifying hope for peace and true progress for humankind.

"In spite of their indisputable contribution to the evolutionary process, the incomparable achievements of scientific knowledge have not really met the innermost needs of the human being who seeks peace. Peace is the sole result of love in its various expressions, from those involving one's own enlightenment to those involving love toward others. This means resignation, selflessness, devotion, and above all, charity in action.

"There is a thirst for harmony within the individual, despite the fact that some are surrounded by all kinds of excesses, thus experiencing the loss of spiritual meaning and, therefore, the peace that only Jesus can provide.

"Hence it is imperative that crusades of love be organized on behalf of all suffering beings on earth, and, at the same time, true fraternity be introduced, without which stability between individuals and nations is impossible.

"Jesus beckons us with His mercy, inviting us to the struggle in His harvest of sacrifice. No one should expect to be rewarded for the work to be performed, or exempt from the cleansing program that the planet is undergoing.

"Personal contribution in the form of dedication to one's duty and the renunciation of destructive selfishness is a must, because the latter has been the ruin of all who evolve heedless of this imminent danger. While the opportunity to serve shines, may this assisting endeavor not be postponed, for it will always be beneficial for the one who offers it.

"We are the sons and daughters of Calvary on the redemptive pathway as we overcome moral imperfections, which must be diluted by the effort of self-enlightenment, while persevering in the struggle against the evil that insists on prevailing in our spiritual nature.

"Every and any expression of love offered to incarnate brothers and sisters becomes a drop of light on our shadowy path, which will be marked by our footprints as we make our way toward the Great Focal Point: the ever-waiting Master of the destitute and unfortunate.

"Let us not rebel against our trials. A life without sacrifice and self-denial is a journey without inner gratitude, directed instead to the land of fantasy, which reality shows to be meaningless... It takes extreme temperatures for metals to be molded into new forms, as it takes polishing for rough gems to be transformed into stars. Likewise, the spirit perfects itself through struggle, beautifying itself and developing the divine light within.

"Like the rest of us, you have been invited to work in His vineyard during these difficult times because you are equipped for the good fight, assisted as you are by your belief in immortality.

"Much will be asked of you because you have received so much help from Heaven. Therefore, enlighten the earth. It is collapsing in anguish and darkness... Only after the peak of the storm do the first manifestations of calm appear.

"You, dear visitors from Alcyone, who have already achieved a state of joy after your harsh trials,[39] will encounter the most cowardly, unexpected traps, and you will be greatly surprised by the primitive methods used by opponents of the truth wishing to impose their lies and illusions... Your words and sentiments will be transformed into weapons with which they will try to strike you, decreasing your ardor in the battle. Understand that these are wicked and unscrupulous combatants, who have absolutely no commitment to ethics or dignity. What is important for them is to defeat you at any cost, and not to self-overcome in order to win other hearts... Their goal is destructive, whereas you are only used to edification.

"You have come from another dimension of our Father's love. You have heard about the moral misery of this earthly grain of cosmic sand, and in your compassion for the inferiority of all of us – its inhabitants and temporary children – you have offered to contribute your sacrifice to promote its ascension on the evolutionary scale of the worlds.

---

[39] They come from a world that is more evolved than the earth, a world that has gone through its own painful evolutionary stages. They have agreed to come to the earth to aid in its planetary transition. – I.R.

"You are welcome, brothers and sisters of mercy and solidarity! We greet you and we thank the Exalted Creator for His unmerited mercy toward us. Raise us from the moral chaos, in which we still languish on our journey toward the peaks of true plenitude.

"We wish you every success under the blessings of Jesus, the Incomparable Builder of School Earth.

"May the serene peace, flowing forth from justice and flawless love, abide with us all.

"With special tenderness and affection, your brother Francis."

When he finished, we could hear the pulse of nature in merriment and the emotion-filled symphony of gratitude vibrating in all of us, the spirits from earth, and the blessed visitors from Alcyone, who also had pearls of tears in their eyes.

With no further comments the meeting ended with a vibrant prayer by our Benefactor Dr. Bezerra, who led us to perfect communion with the thought of Jesus.

The Angel of Assisi and his companions entered the tube of light and returned to their dwelling in the higher spheres.

The teams in charge of the still-incarnate brothers and sisters stood by their side and prepared to take them back to their homes, enabling them to have a fragmentary memory of the events of that unforgettable evening.

We would soon initiate new endeavors, a minor contribution to building the new world now under full construction.

CHAPTER 16

AMID THE GREAT PLANETARY TRANSITION

The next morning, our group met in the shade of a beautiful oak in the city park, where children were playing, watched over by their nannies as people hurried by in pursuit of their usual duties and commitments.

The sun shone a gentle gold on the green foliage of the old trees kissing the delicate flowers and the well-manicured grass.

Fragrances in the arms of the breeze fraternized with the onomatopoeia of nature in celebration.

Infused with the love of the *Poverello,* we did not have the courage to break the pervading harmony with any of the questions flogging our minds.

In this orchestrated environment of blessings in the out-of-doors, Dr. Bezerra took in the busy human landscape with a sweet look of tenderness and compassion, considering:

"The earth's population has reached the significant number of seven billion reincarnated beings vying for the opportunity to evolve...

"In spite of the great acquisitions of technological knowledge and the advances of science in a number of areas, transcendent values in these troubled days have not received appropriate consideration by scholars dedicated to analyzing and promoting human resources. They are more concerned with techniques than with moral behavior, which is of paramount importance. Therefore the inheritance to be handed down to the new generations inhabiting the planet is more about greed, the pleasure of the physical senses, and gaining recognition by any means possible, giving rise to violence and disorder...

"The contempt of many leaders and of countless opinion multipliers for the religions of the past, and the fanaticism that has developed around spiritualism for gain, encouraging the amassing of monetary resources and favoring with health those who can afford to buy it, have given way to materialism and utilitarianism, instead of solidarity, compassion and the spirit of fraternity, especially given the difficulty of the authentic experience of love as taught and lived by Jesus.

"We can say we are experiencing a period of extravagance and immediate gratification, without measuring the pernicious consequences.

"Individuals seem anesthetized with regard to the treasures of the soul, with a few exceptions, and even among those who have embraced the Spiritist revelation, conflicts of various orders act as mechanisms against selflessness and total commitment to the Messiah from Nazareth.

"Some individuals, who see themselves as bold and skeptical, do not take into account the events that are plaguing the planet, be they the ever-increasingly powerful and tragic seismic convulsions, or those of a terrifying sociological, economic/financial, psychological, or ethical/moral nature. Others, more timid, let themselves be seduced by fundamentalist religious teachings, and are frightened and anxious about the prospect of the end of the world.

"Fixed dates are set with some levity, as if some cosmic cataclysm is going to occur as punishment for a society that has grown distant from God – a kind of absurd vengeance... Such people do not know the extent of our Father's love. They expect Him to unleash His wrath as the ultimate process, as if life actually ended with physical death.

"Fortunately the end of the world that the prophecies speak of refers to one of a moral nature, of course, with inevitable tragedies that will strike entire communities, providing social renewal, which the absence of Love cannot achieve as one would wish... These phenomena are not fatalistically scheduled for this or that period, but for a lengthy period of transformations, adaptations and events that foster order and solidarity among all beings.

"It is therefore understandable that the most serious occurrence is, in a way, dependent on the free will of human beings, whose behavior can hasten, slow, or even modify its conditions, either mitigating or aggravating it...

"Someone has rightly defined the universe as being one great thought because everything in it vibrates, is reflected in its structure, and contributes to its preservation or disarray.

"Trying to define a particular period is foolhardy due to the daily events that will be responsible for future occurrences.

"If instead of cultivating selfishness, folly and wickedness human minds would emit waves of kindness, compassion, love and mercy, it would certainly change the phenomena scheduled for the major change already underway.

"Extremely powerful planetary convulsions are necessary for there to be a change for the better concerning the climate, the relative stability of the major tectonic plates, and in social and community organizations, with natural agrarian and nutritional resources to sustain future populations, which will be neither starving nor destitute, unlike today...

"As humans come to terms with the transience of physical life, the planet's psychosphere will be very different because the thoughts that are emitted will alter current vibrational bands, which will in turn contribute to the harmony of all, as well as the use of the time available in joyful preparation for facing the change that will take place for many through discarnation, taking them to another arena of reality.

"Our Father's love and Jesus' tenderness toward His flock will lessen the gravity of the events, as will compassion and mercy, in spite of the severity of the law of progress.

"All of us, whether discarnate or incarnate, have been entrusted with the planetary transition to a better world. And that is why all of us must also commit ourselves to our own inner moral transformation, enveloping ourselves in light so that no darkness can trouble us or lead us to hinder the march of evolution.

"Indeed, due to their primitivism, spirits still holding on to degrading passions will attune to different vibratory waves characteristic of lower-order worlds, to which they will transfer because of such attunement. There they will become helpful workers due to the resources they already possess in relation to those primitive worlds, where they will learn the lessons of humility and good conduct. Everything is linked together in the divine laws. No one is ever lacking in lofty resources for the moral development of their spirit. During that immense molecular transformation process, up to the moment in which angelhood is reached, there are favorable means for intellectual and moral growth, without harsh punitive measures or lamentable privileges granted to some at the expense of others.

"In this sense, spirit communications through mediumship represent a valuable contribution to corporeal travelers by showing them immortality, divine justice, the mechanisms for getting the most out of the reincarnation experience, and the immense significance of every moment in life.

"It will be easier for us to encourage them to learn through love rather than through suffering, inviting them to reflection and to the work of fraternal charity, which will enrich them and prepare them for inevitable release through discarnation, whenever it happens."

Everything was a festival of color and light, noise and movement, as Dr. Bezerra paused for a moment before continuing:

"To praise and thank the Lord of the Universe for the glory of the life He has given to us, and to beseech Him to help us be faithful to the postulates of the thought of Jesus, our Master and Guide – that is our duty at all times.

"Thus devoted mediums and promoters of the good in all walks of life will experience the sting of difficulty, and will suffer derision and rampant misunderstanding, reinforced by invigilance.

"It is not surprising that the best sentiments of all those who work for Jesus are distorted and become instruments of affliction.

"Love, when authentic, bears witness to its faithfulness. Nowadays, true Christians still comprise a small group, reminiscent of the period of harsh trials during the first three centuries of spreading the message of Jesus throughout the Roman Empire.

"All of them will be called to make some form of sacrifice in order to demonstrate the excellence of the evangelical content, considering, on one hand, the personal requirements that demand reparation, and on the other, faithfulness, which requires confirmation through example. Let no one marvel at the unexpected difficulties that so often cause surprise and anguish.

"Every commitment to the good produces an equivalent reaction, which is overcome by the spirit of selflessness.

"We are all filled with admiration and are moved when we consider the greatness of the martyrs of the past, but when called on to proceed with our own witness, we do not always behave as expected. Therefore prayer is a sure place to rebuild our strength and proceed with joy.

"Entities who delight in the pleasure of vampirizing energies from distracted, foolish incarnates naturally oppose the messengers of Jesus wherever they are, generating conflicts around them and furiously assailing them. Instead of being sad and disenchanted, these workers should focus on the joy of serving and, without any display of masochism, thank heaven for the self-enlightening opportunity.

"Undoubtedly, at a time of great change, as is happening right now, suffering is always greater and more acute as old habits must give way to the new demands of progress. Thus it is natural that the generating forces of anarchy and calamity, sensing that they are being fought on all fronts, make use of every mechanism available to keep things as they are. So it is understandable that all those who are devoted to dignifying human values be seen as enemies that must be opposed.

"Consequently, any suffering for love of the ideal of truth in the construction of a new world is an honor for us.

"May we be characterized by superior discernment, and may our most valuable resources be at the behest of the Lord of the Vineyard leading the way."

After a timely silence, he concluded:

"New activities await us. Let us go!"

We headed for a lovely place adorned by a huge, white sand beach, pounded by the white foam of the serene ocean waves...

At some distance we saw a beautiful, colossal fluidic construction, almost as large as a city in the spirit world, with many industrious spirits moving about.

A peculiar luminosity shone from the buildings, denoting the excellence of the activities taking place there. A projection of a special kind of light enveloped the city, defining its contours, which constituted an impediment to any kind of invasion by low-order beings.

Noticing our amazement and enchantment, Dr. Bezerra explained:

"That is a community reserved for preparing our brothers and sisters from Alcyone, those who have applied to reincarnate on the earth.

"By general choice it is called 'Sanctuary of Hope' because it is from some of these communities that the builders of the New Era have departed for commitments on our lovely planet, whereas other missionaries returning from the past will come directly from their realms of light to immerse themselves in the physical world.

"In view of the vibratory stage of the sphere whence they come, these brothers and sisters of hope need to make a number of perispiritual adjustments to be compatible with earth's constraints, as well as to adapt to the psychosphere of their new temporary residence.

"Sanctuaries like this one have been built since the end of the last century, when they began to host our benevolent benefactor friends in many countries of our beloved orb.

"Considering that missionaries will be reincarnating in the most diverse areas of knowledge, as well as in various sectors of society, those who come from outside our system have to go through a phase of perispiritual adaptation for the success of their particular undertaking.

"They are submitting themselves to special procedures so that adapting to their new body will be less painful. Having lived in a sphere where pain and physical ailments no longer exist as purifying measures, it is essential that they condense energies in their perispirit suitable for earth habitation.

"This voluntary endeavor out of love is also sacrificial since it is much more rewarding to ascend to higher planes of life, whereas descending into the 'caves of trial' is a real challenge.

"By reflecting on it, one can get a vague idea of what it meant for Jesus to plunge into the deep darkness and heavy energies of our planet when He came to teach us the sublime processes of love and elevation. As a consequence, He always reserved regular periods of His time to pray and meditate in order to stay attuned to the Father, whether in the desert or in busy urban areas with His disciples, maintaining significant and invaluable times of silence for the continuity of His incomparable mission."

He paused for a moment due to our amazement.

I must confess that I myself had been completely unaware of the existence of these noble communities scattered across the beloved planet, serving as special laboratories for the reincarnation of selfless visitors.

But as I thought about the process, I could see that it was very logical, because for us Terrestrials to descend into the realm of water we need suitable equipment. The same applies when we go beyond the realm of oxygen surrounding the planet, as astronauts do...

My mind began to generate questions and a lot of curiosity ensued about the learning experience possible for us on our visit to that blessed center of special preparation.

Dr. Bezerra continued:

"The process of transition has been going on for quite some time, with specific phases: seismic events, which have occurred in all eras, but which are now much more frequent; mental suffering resulting from unhealthy situations generated by human beings themselves as they have chosen the more difficult path; cruel diseases that find room for expansion amongst those who are receptive to them; collective suffering as a result of the subaltern interests of despots, the ambitious, tormenters of humanity, assisted by other tormenters who keep them in their unhappy condition...

"...And other similar afflictions, inviting all individuals to reflect on the changes that are taking place now and which will continue with even more severity.

"It is only natural for the Lord Jesus to have provided for the return of His messengers, those who marked their era with the characteristics of love and wisdom so as to boost humankind's progress towards this culminating moment, and who are needed now for the great confrontation with the unhealthy legacies remaining in the planet's psychosphere due to the primitive condition of some of its inhabitants.

"Concomitantly the presence of missionaries from another dimension is essential. Side by side, they can defeat the schemes and plans of moral disasters by modifying the planet's moral structure, which will ascend to a situation more proper for a world of regeneration.

"Let us visit this sanctuary of blessed activities for the future of terrestrial humanity."

My imagination could never have conceived of a city as beautiful and landscaped as this one.

A sweet fragrance was carried lightly by the breeze of the day.

A peculiar light that had not originated with the sun bathed everything we could see.

The activity was significant, much like that of a regular medium-sized city.

Large buildings, but not too tall, were everywhere, charming the entire urban landscape with their original forms, adorned with gardens planted with trees unknown to me. Vehicles different from ours floated above the ground in balanced movement, without exaggerated speed. Beautifully plumed songbirds would sometimes cut through the air, beautifying nature, itself enriched with colorful images.

We were warmly and cheerfully received by a noble spirit waiting for us at the entryway.

Without articulated speech, Dr. Bezerra introduced our small group and we were able to perceive the receptionist's thought as he greeted us kindly.

I was truly amazed by the events taking place in a kaleidoscope of rare beauty.

It was the first time such a thing had ever happened to me. Thinking without much effort, the sounds to be emitted would be put forth from the mind in inner modulations that were captured by all of us.

When I lived on the earth I often wondered what communication in the higher spheres of life would be like. Now I was able to actually go through the enchanting experience.

Incidentally, as I mentioned in another book, the spirits had the usual terrestrial characteristics, without any exotic shape or color, a little thinner and of average height – roughly 5 feet, 11 inches – with harmony of form and unusual beauty, radiating engaging sympathy.

We were led down a wide, well-designed avenue lined with quadrangular buildings composed of a fluidic material that allowed us to see inside some of them. Others brought to mind American universities whose buildings were spread out across an enormous campus.

We enjoyed a pleasant walk of a little more than a hundred meters[40] to the wide entryway of a large three-story building, where we could see some of the very well-equipped rooms. We went up to the second floor and were greeted by a friendly group of scholars in the field of the perispirit.

Our escort introduced us to the supervisor of this research center, informing him that we were one of many groups responsible for disclosing the presence of workers from Alcyone in the planet's future.

With special deference to our mentor and kindness toward us, the director explained the need for the visitors from another dimension to adjust to the planetary conditions in which they would be operating.

We were led into another room, where we observed a large number of spirits in deep concentration under a powerful jet of luminous energy. In that state, concentrating on the objectives that had brought them to Earth, they developed features of perispiritual expandability – their perispirits having been almost entirely absorbed by the spirit – in order to be able to shape the necessities typical of the corporeal vehicle they would be using during their reincarnational mission.

---

[40] App. 109 yards. – I.R.

As spirits progress, the functions of the intermediate body[41] are slowly absorbed by the immortal being due to the needlessness of constructing corruptible, degenerate, limited bodies that bear the signs of the evolutionary process... Having achieved a higher level, the spirit being undergoes rebirth by means of automatism, taking the healthy and beautiful, ever-more subtle and noble form as its model, until it attains the state of plenitude, the *Kingdom of Heaven* within...

That delicate operation of perispiritual remolding was providing the spirits from Alcyone with a psychical return to the period when their incarnations were painful, and, as such, imprinted with the evolutionary needs on the delicate tissues of their perispirits' structure.

A large number of spirits were involved in the process of perispiritual recuperation according to earthly molds. At the same time, delicate instruments attached to the head were transmitting events of our orb so they could get accustomed to everyday occurrences, thus facilitating their interaction with other members of the large human family into which they would be born.

All this information was transmitted to us mentally in a remarkable process of telepathy, as is often the case in certain interventions of spirit-related work, enabling us to capture the thoughts of our mentors and even events that had taken place in patients' lives.

The sense of harmony during that exchange truly touched us and explained so much more than words could ever have.

Hence all questions disappeared, for as we received information, we also automatically received clarification without having to ask for it.

---

[41] i.e. the perispirit – I.R.

Dr. Bezerra, who was certainly familiar with the whole procedure, having been the intermediary for leading us to that center of such achievements, emitted waves of well-being and joy. He also spoke to us about the earth of tomorrow, when suffering would beat a retreat and individuals, turned to the good, would enjoy the gifts of harmony.

We had been instructed by the noble scientist for about two hours, when we were told it was time to leave.

Our beloved benefactor thanked him on behalf of all of us for his kind deference, and we were led back to the entryway of that fascinating city of hope, where we joyfully said our goodbyes.

As we were returning to our support Center, Dr. Bezerra explained that these buildings, similar to the fluidic construction of the watchtower at the Love and Charity Spiritist Center, had been designed and built by engineers from Alcyone. They had created them before the arrival of those who would reincarnate as places where they could prepare themselves in order to be able to travel through the earth's psychosphere later, communicating mediumistically and participating in spiritual endeavors...

Veritable avenues of communication between Alcyone and Earth had been opened, overcoming the colossal distance so that the exchange could be made safely, using specific resources of volitation...

FINAL ACTIVITIES

Time was pressing and the activities were ongoing.

Waves of sufferers looking for help flocked to the Spiritist Center as the time came closer for our return to our colony.

Countless assistance activities were performed in those days, with visits to a number of Centers that had suffered the pernicious injunctions of the shrewd persecutor. Some of them were still feeling the thorns of suffering and tribulation, which would certainly demand a period of afflictive experiences before they could recover.

When one does not listen to or follow the guideline of love, suffering steps in as the grand master that corrects and guides, polishing the diamond in the rough into a blazing star. And even if this process takes a very long time, it winds up producing the beneficial results that everyone desires.

The Love and Charity Spiritist Center had been recomposed. Anacleto had awakened to the reality of his duties and had returned to being the same diligent and dedicated worker as before, having left everybody with the lesson that no one is exempt from the wicked assaults of the darkness and abysmal falls into error due to a mind shift. One must always be vigilant in the correct fulfillment of one's duties.

Martina had found the path of inner enlightenment and was caring for her pregnancy with unparalleled tenderness and devotion, touching us with her daily renewal.

The schedule regarding the workers from Alcyone who were immersing themselves in the earth's atmosphere for the sublime endeavor of the planetary transition was proceeding smoothly, delineating new commitments whose fruits were already showing up in the social behavior of a few idealists, initiating the Era of Peace, which, although still delayed, was already showing signs of elevation and harmony.

In the meantime, Dr. Bezerra explained his wishes on that penultimate night of our special endeavor. We would be visiting one of the darkest parts of the city.

"The earth – he explained – is experiencing a period of drug addiction, evoking the symbolic figure of one of the four horsemen of John's Apocalypse, since children and young people are the most-affected, defenseless victims, although the epidemic has reached all age levels and social groups.

"Our hearts are broken by the deplorable situation of addicts that have let themselves be afflicted by a moral disease that destroys them in a perverse and ongoing way. We have visited these unhappy places where the borders of the spirit world intermix with those of the material world in a nefarious exchange of exhaustion and madness.

"Thus I would like us to visit the local so-called 'Crack Land.' Such places have been carved out in the hearts of the big cities, and are well-known by authorities and other persons who are powerless to eradicate them. Veritable punitive regions on the earth, they are redoubts of misery and perversion, demonstrating the inferiority of our beloved planet and the superlative sufferings of the spirits that seek them out.

"Let us put on compassion and charity as we enter this community of unfortunates, and guided by the lofty purposes of assistance and spiritual tenderness, let us ask ourselves in the depths of our soul: What would Jesus do in our stead if He were here?

"And since He is sending us in His place, we must do all we can, as closely as possible to His sublime approach. Let us pray in preparation for the work ahead, when the largest number of victims will be present."

In response to our mentor's invitation, we prayed in silence, seeking the most appropriate attunement with the affable Master of Nazareth.

At 11:00 p.m. we headed for the center of the city, crossing streets and avenues still bustling with the great excitement of people and the busy traffic.

In a dark area of a narrow street located between two broad avenues, where filth and despair predominated, we were faced with a heartrending scene.

Fierce-looking incarnate traffickers and animal-like entities, unrecognizable as the discarnate human beings they actually were, mingled together in a terrible fight over territory, while nearby, young men and women offered themselves to the market of the vilest prostitution in order to get money for their destructive addiction.

Some so-called "street children" were embroiled in a fight over leftover crack in makeshift pipes or on wooden boxes that served as tables. They were staggering, almost completely wasted by the destructive poison.

Some were squalid; others had wasted away, child-like wraiths walking around and going through trash cans, lying on filthy mats or sheets of torn cardboard made into fetid beds amid voracious rats...

Most terrifying were the spiritual landscape and morbific emanations by the discarnates coupled to the perispirits of those who had become their victims, their energies usurped by the fumes from the outrageous drug.

Ever since the area had been geared to the destruction of lives, it had become a hellish site, with the pathological characteristics of other places in the spirit world, outside the earth; veritable *hells,* where miserable beings suffered hardships resulting from their past wretched behavior.

The leaden sky was lit up from time to time by lightning from ominous storms... Destructive magnetic discharges filled the air while horror prevailed everywhere.

Heated arguments continuously broke out between users and *mules* – young people who moved the drugs – over new quotas or some payment not made for previous debts, often resulting in physical fights entailing immense harm to both parties. Cruel spirits were satisfied by and encouraged these contentions, which they regarded as pleasing shows of madness.

Mightn't this situation be the absolute bottom of the well, the lowest degree of human degradation, if such ever existed?!

It was not our place, however, to judge or analyze what we were observing. We were to show compassion to all the sufferers writhing there in despair, causing spontaneous tears to stream down my face.

Now and then an outburst of hysterical screams would erupt, terrible pleas in the irreversible turmoil of some of the deranged, mocked by discarnates who also exploited them.

Dr. Bezerra gathered us in the middle of the dark, narrow street occupied by the crowd of mental and spiritual patients. Raising his voice, he began a prayer:

"Lord of mercy!

"Have compassion on all of us, exiled rebel children who have abandoned the pathway traced out by our Father. We have chosen the winding paths of suffering, and have fallen into the deep chasms of madness.

"Yesterday, fascinated by power and emotionally unstructured to wield it, we indebted ourselves terribly with many lives which we reaped with cruelty; with lives we misused in the zest of our pride; with hearts we broke, eager to submit them to our whims; with brothers and sisters on the earthly journey, whom we turned into unfortunate slaves. Today, we have returned, bearing indescribable, profound guilt and inextricable torment as remorseful children trying to escape responsibility through the anesthetics of illusion...

"And in doing so, thinking of relieving the anguish that has wounded our sentiments, we have immersed ourselves deeper in the pestilent swamps of self-destruction and obsessions imposed on us by the victims awaiting us beyond the portico of the fleeting physical body...

"Here we are, in a deplorable situation, not only unable to recover from our crimes, but worsening our situation because of our contempt for your laws of mercy but also of justice.

"In this alliance of individuals demented with hatred and fear, we have lost our way. We cannot know where our options start, since we live under the hammers of those who have been associated with us since those unhappy days, desperately seeking to do justice... But how can they, if they are all as wretched as we are – the ones responsible for their misfortune?

"Have mercy on us, O Clement and Righteous One. Let Your love go beyond the limits of established laws and reach us so that we may rehabilitate ourselves by following Your lessons of eternal life and compassion...

"Help us, O Lord of the wayward and forgotten of the world!

"Repeat Your stay amongst us of two thousand years ago, when all had forsaken us, and when You rescued us with your matchless love by coming to us in these dens of misery!

"Help us to help others with Your sublime compassion."

When he had finished, his voice cracking and his eyes moist, a soft light started to shine on the terrible den. A large number of benevolent spirits appeared from the diminishing thick mist, intent on assisting those who lay in torpor on the ground, briefly freeing a few addicts from their spirit-obsessors, driving away some of the traffickers, and applying vigorous energies to everyone present.

Invited to take part, we approached our sick brothers and sisters, and began to send them our energies as we prayed for their inner renewal.

Our brother Jésus, deeply moved, remembering the days when leprosy had taken up residence in his body, attended to the oldest patients with immense tenderness, seeing drug addiction like the leprosy of old, in that it degrades, banishes from social interaction, perverts and drives its victims insane.

Bearer of outstanding moral and spiritual values, this now-redeemed disciple of Jesus proceeded to speak to some of the vengeful brothers and sisters, showing them the need for compassion and forgiveness. He told them about his own experience in centuries gone by, when he too had succumbed to power and ambition, virtually insane, until the moment Jesus invited him to redemption on the cross of untold suffering...

He told them that in nameless suffering he had found the peace he longed for, which was why he was now seeking others like him in order to help them recover their peace of mind.

Many spirits were touched by his poetic, sweet speech, by the harmonic vibrations he emitted as he invoked Jesus' protection for all, as well as the Blessed Mother's in order to gather to Her bosom those unfortunate children, who chose to remain in ignorance and rebellion...

We were all touched with the blessing of work in that place of suffering profoundly ignored by a society that despised those who escaped there in exhaustion and madness.

In the meantime our attention was drawn to a young man about twenty years old. Trembling with a fever, his eyes were dilated in the ecstasy of the drug. He was also convulsing... When we approached him, Dr. Bezerra psychically informed us that it was time for him to discarnate in light of the tuberculosis that had defeated him while the crack consumed his last bit of energy.

All of a sudden he expelled a gush of blood, and then amid indefinably agonizing death throes he began to discarnate, victimized by terrible hemoptysis which satisfied a number of spirits deformed by lycanthropy.

That is when a discarnate woman tenderly approached and stayed at his side, tenderly calling him her darling child, waiting for the process to end, now under the guidance of our mentor who drove away the vile spirit-enemies besetting him up until that critical time...

After a few minutes, organic death took place, but there were still a few ties to the spent body. They would dissolve slowly toward complete discarnation sometime later.

From that moment on, however, he would be cared for by his mother, who had often visited him in that dreadful place, unable to assist him as efficiently as she desired.

Assisted by the visiting benefactors, a young woman who had just given herself to a drunk in order to get enough money for another hit began to cry and wake up from under the anesthesia of the hallucinatory drug. Then she ran from the hideous place, not knowing what was happening to her...

The assistance lasted for over an hour, until silence fell over the area and the tormented individuals stopped arriving...

The soft light remained, as did a large number of the benevolent assisting visitors, whose further assistance escaped our observation. And since we were unable to contribute more effectively, we offered intercessory prayers so that the improved ambient conditions would remain for all those misguided brothers and sisters who had adopted the unsolvable solution that complicated their moral debts even more... But we all have free will, and our choices are respected until the moment we abandon our inferiority through redemptive expiations.

A few vengeful spirits were invited to follow us to the Spiritist Center, assisted as we were by friends who had answered our prayer to the Lord and who served there, for there is not one spot where the mercy of the good, even if unnoticed, does not glimmer.

That very morning, with Hermano's assistance, those wretched brothers and sisters were given shelter and would be attended to according to the circumstances and the possibilities at the proper time.

After thanking the coworkers from the spirit world, Dr. Bezerra displayed great joy resulting from the recent labor of love.

We spent the last day in a meeting with Hermano and other spirit workers from the Love and Charity Spiritist Center. We also visited some of the institutions that were part of our program.

I was filled with a mixture of tenderness and gratitude, of anticipated longing and joy at the prospect of one more task completed.

CHAPTER 18

FINAL ENDEAVORS AND GOODBYES

On that last night of our special service stay, after the institution's usual activities, when everyone had gone home for a good night's rest, the farewell meeting began, marked by assisting some of the discarnate brothers and sisters brought there from Crack Land.

The mediums Celestina and Marcos, the psychotherapist to discarnates Marcelo, plus a few of the Center's coworkers were brought with Hermano's help to the mediumistic room in partial disengagement through sleep so that they could attend to some of the brothers and sisters in need of spiritual help.

After a heartfelt prayer by Dr. Bezerra, Celestina went into deep trance to become an instrument for one of the deformed spirits writhing in the throes of resentment and dependency on the terrible fumes of addiction he was absorbing through his victim.

Mentally urged to cooperate, brother Petitinga began to apply passes of fluidic detoxification. He also intensified the donation of energies to Celestina so that she would not be harmed by the communicating spirit's terrible mental fixations.

Very slowly, the miserable spirit began experiencing a slight change in his perispiritual structure, thanks to his contact with the dedicated medium, who provided him the model for correcting his form while, through great effort, he used her vocal chords to ask:

"What's... happening?

Meanwhile Euripides had entered the circle with a young woman who was asleep and in a deplorable state of physical, emotional and mental debilitation.

She was awakened with great affection by our friend, who had placed her on a padded chaise longue, where she could recline in relative repose.

Much weakened, she was looking around in wonder when a young spirit approached and tenderly embraced her, saying:

"Trust in God, Vivianne, so you can exit the abyss in which you find yourself."

The voice, spoken with immense tenderness, resounded within her and sharpened her memory, causing the woman to stare at her visitor. She recognized her as someone who was very dear and she immediately began to weep.

As the two held hands in a gesture of affection and transmission of security, Petitinga answered the first spirit:

"We are in a hospital for the critically ill."

"No... I'm... sick... and ... miserable."

"Yes," replied Dr. Bezerra, we know that, and that is why we have brought you here for treatment. Your misery is the misery of a rebellious soul that has refused to submit to the Divine Laws for having chosen the harshest and cruelest way to solve problems that love could have solved if you had acted otherwise."

"I've had no ... other ... choice."

As the mediumistic trance deepened, the communicating spirit became more lucid and better able to express himself.

"There's always a choice," explained Dr. Bezerra, "when you desire the good and not evil, retribution, revenge or the madness of wicked selfishness."

"I was murdered... That tramp took part in the plot and I can't let her go unpunished, because there is no justice on earth and she got away with her heinous crime..."

"Oh, but you're wrong, my brother. Earthly justice is still the fruit of the imperfection of those who draw up laws that favor their own corrupt interests... Even so, the conscience of each and every one of us is engraved with the laws of life, which have established the codes for decent behavior and higher justice. So we are not free of the consequences of our errors and crimes, even if we are not reached immediately by human penal measures. Moreover we cannot escape from ourselves and our own responsibility. As you know, life is not extinguished when the body dies.

"Thus when those who have suffered injustice in the world wake up in the reality beyond the grave, it is not right for them to take the dagger of justice into their own hands to do justice according to their passions, committing similar or worse wrongs of injustice and wickedness."

"Yes... I wish that were so... But that's not what happens... Victim that I was... of the woman I loved ... I followed her success in the world... while the vermin consumed me... leading me to unending madness... But I survived... and now I'm doing justice."

"What you are doing is not justice; it's revenge. And every act of revenge just leads to worse dramas disrespectful of the Divine Laws.

"Vivianne was reborn to redeem her tempestuous moral slide. She didn't bear any of the physical marks of her nefarious conduct, but in the core of her inner being she bore the memories of her error, guilt and regret, making her sad, lonely and miserable ever since her childhood... Feeling anguished, but not grasping the reason for her misfortune, she attracted you with her thoughts, in keeping with the sovereign laws that, where the offender is, there the victim will be too...

"You were supposed to sympathize with her misfortune and help her rehabilitation through good deeds so that she could emerge from the chaos of error and reach the realm of moral elevation. But you did just the opposite. When you recognized her you made her sorrows worse through hypnosis, fixing your sick thoughts on her, making her even more miserable and causing her to leave home in emotional distress, driving her to that den whence she has just been taken by the mercy of Jesus Christ.

"But because God's love has no boundaries, this is the moment that you, too, deserve compassion and help, enjoying the blessing of awakening to a new reality which will provide you with peace and a new start under new conditions favorable to reaching plenitude."

"I just can't... forgive her."

"You don't have to this very minute. But at least grant her the right to expound the issue from her own point of view since every event has two sides... All right?"

Immediately thereafter, supported by Euripides' gentle arm, the incarnate young woman, in partial disengagement from her physical body, was moved toward her obsessor. When she recognized him she let out a cry of horror.

"Michel! Oh, my God! Please don't kill me. Leave me in peace, even though I don't deserve it."

She continued in emotional and verbal disarray, while Euripides strengthened her spirit with calming and renewing energies.

"I'm not a murderer! I'm the victim of a wicked plot. Have mercy, dear God! Oh, how I've suffered!"

When addressed by name by the dazed woman, Michel retaliated with blasphemies and terrifying threats, jolting the medium and foaming with rage, with eyes almost out of their sockets.

It was the first time the two spirits had confronted each other, even though whenever she had disengaged from her physical body due to the impact of illicit drugs, she would meet him and run around aimlessly until waking up exhausted, in need of another hit.

"Listen to me, please; just this once," she cried!

Mocking her with immense disdain, but under Dr. Bezerra's telementalization, Michel complied with a look of cynical contempt.

"I always loved you and showed it all the time we were living together... You wrecked our peace when you brought home that viper who hypnotized me, that horrible Antoine de Val... He said he was your friend, but he was a wicked criminal who just wanted our things and to cause my downfall."

She could not go on, because Michel interrupted her scornfully:

"If you knew... that... why did you betray me... and help him murder me?" He burst into sobs of despair.

"Listen to me; in all that, I'm the one who's been miserable. I don't deny that I was thoughtless and condescending with that criminal. I even went so far as to encourage him in my emptiness as a foolish woman, but I made sure it did not go too far. That was my big mistake, the folly that has been eating me away, and right here and now I have come to realize that that is why I've always been an emotional wreck...

"Bit by bit, while you were out taking care of the vineyard, he would skillfully seduce me. I tried to talk to you more than once but you avoided the subject, distrustful, as if I didn't deserve any consideration... Those were awful days... The First World War had begun and France was in it...

"In our beloved region of Champagne-Ardenne, the call to the war was staggering. And Antoine, who was unemployed and living at your expense, was summoned to Paris to enroll in the army..."

Vivianne made a long and painful pause while tears streamed down her gaunt face.

Then she continued:

"On the day before his departure you yourself hosted a party in honor of the criminal. And after everyone had left he got you and me drunk. He also slipped you a sedative and you passed out on our bed...

"The villain assaulted me and stole our best things: money, jewelry and other valuables, and then stabbed you to death and took off without our employees ever knowing what had happened in our chateaux...

"When I came to, I couldn't remember what had happened, except that I had been victim of a physical assault.

"The scandal was terrible: extensive police investigations, with attempts to implicate me; searches for the fugitive, who had soon thereafter left for the front on the Maginot Line, on the border with Germany... where he died in combat, without having enjoyed the fruits of his spoils...

"I only found out about it years later, when I was old and living in Paris off of some money I got from selling the property, the money having been split between your family and me.

"My life was an endless torment and I began using absinthe, which was the fad at the time. It gradually consumed me, until death snatched my body. But that didn't give me peace.

"I reincarnated, in a miserable state, supported by Giselle, who had been your sister and always my friend, and who died before the tragedy that befell you and me. She's here, helping me right now."

"What else can I say, except to beg for you to show mercy to both of us?!"

Michel was shocked since he had not known about the facts of the matter. He had not yet recovered from his surprise, when Giselle spoke to him with great tenderness:

"Michel, I'm here in our mother's name to fetch you so you can be born again on our old lands, now under new ownership, and rebuild your road of purification. Today, Antoine is the property's owner, and he's tormented and unhappy. You will return to physical life as his son... You must reincarnate through him."

The young woman radiated a magnificent light and her speech was soft and penetrating, profoundly affecting Michel.

Lacking the control needed in circumstances of such magnitude, he wanted to throw himself into his sister's arms. Unable to do so since he was speaking through a medium, he shouted:

"Please help me, angel of our lives. You have always been Jesus' emissary on earth! Forgive me for my lunacy and lessen the burning madness that has consumed me for almost an eternity."

"Trust in God, dear brother, and have the courage to start over!"

She approached him and wrapped him in immense tenderness as Dr. Bezerra put him to sleep with a soothing and loving voice, then took him to another room in our sphere.

The environment soon returned to its usual harmony after the removal of Michel, his sister, and Vivianne, whom Hermano transferred to an adjoining room in order to take her back to her body in Crack Land, where she was having a reinvigorating dream that would be beneficial to her and help her get out of that ghetto of misery. Giselle would inspire her and continue to assist her…

The limit of love is the Infinite, without a doubt. Love solves all the afflicting problems ever heard about.

There were other pain-filled spirit communications, and after the sanctifying endeavor of charity, with the mediums and the counselor returning to complete lucidity, we heard the voices of spirits singing in the environment, now transformed into a Greek amphitheater.

I realized that the *Watchtower* had been dismantled as it was no longer necessary, and that several members of the Spiritist Center had been brought in for the final phase.

A sweet fragrance permeated the environment.

The room had taken on a grandiose aspect reminiscent of the enclosure where we had had the meeting on our plane before our trip to the earth. I must confess that I am profoundly amazed by the power of the Lord's Messengers as they manipulate energies and shape everything that they need to condense on our plane.

It was in this environment that a beautiful jet of light fell on the main platform, and we saw St. Francis materialize, assisted by two of his companions from his early days in Assisi.

The simplicity and emanations of peace of the Poverello enraptured our sentiments while the tenderness and unction of his companions penetrated us in a very special way.

Stepping outside the shaft of light, he smiled at the audience, and with an indescribable voice that sounded like a canticle of love, he prayed:

"Divine Shepherd of terrestrial souls!

"Out of Your mercy and compassion, come into this abyss in order to rescue us from the cliffs we are holding on to before our final fall.

"Transform Your cross of love into a bridge to lead us from the morass to the saving plateau for our deliverance.

"Extend Your crown of thorns transformed into powerful links in the safety chain to unite ours to Your sublime existence.

"Widen Your gaze over an earth in painful transition, to reduce its widespread suffering, inviting those who weep to remember the Supreme Good, inspiring in them the yearning for peace and the blessedness that will soon take over the planet.

"Aid the guests from another dimension as they reincarnate for the endeavor of the enlightening experience of the world so that they can inscribe on the orb's still-dark landscape the indefinable light of hope and complete fraternity.

"Take our noblest thoughts and braid the wreath of wisdom that must grace our brow, helping us with all our immortal decisions.

"O Holy One, confer on us Your blessing of love so that our path of briars may become a pathway of sublimation.

"...And forgive us for our pettiness and poverty, without anything to offer, except our own being in service in Your Name.

"Deliver us, O Lord of the dawn of the Resurrection, so that we may overcome death, suffering and fear in order to serve You forever.

"So be it!"

The sublime music that remained in the air, and the scent that dominated the room, as if derived from fresh roses on a mellow spring morning, would remain impregnated forever in our minds.

The vision of that unparalleled moment would remain on our mental screen forever after.

In silence crowned with tears, we said goodbye to Hermano, who thanked Dr. Bezerra and the rest of us for our labor. We embraced everybody who had taken part in the endeavor of illumination on both planes of life. And as our silence sang our gratitude, our little caravan returned to our beautiful dwelling in the spirit world as the group separated under the blessings of the dawn of the New Era.

Before we parted ways in our community, we looked at the beloved planet haloed in the light of the stars, and I cannot deny the fact that only tears could speak words impossible to enunciate.

A wave of nostalgia, tenderness and gratitude came over all of us while we reaffirmed our vows to love and serve tirelessly under the blessings of Jesus.

THE END

85642029R00121

Made in the USA
Lexington, KY
03 April 2018